FALSE CONFESSIONS

OF A

TRUE HOLLYWOOD SCREENWRITER

A book by Sharon Y. Cobb

Written by Sharon Y. Cobb

Directed by Sharon Y. Cobb

Produced by Sharon Y. Cobb

Published July 2011 by Hollywood Hills Publishing
Cover design by Susan Karasic.

Library of Congress Cataloging-in-Publication Data
    False Confessions of a True Hollywood Screenwriter / Sharon Y. Cobb — 1st edition
    ISBN 978-0-9838016-1-0

ACKNOWLEDGEMENTS

An enthusiastic thank you to all the agents, managers, entertainment attorneys, Hollywood producers, studio suits and film stars who love, love, loved my work but who didn't decide to represent me or buy my work. You inspired me to write this book. Without you, I would still be a baby writer with rose-colored glasses. Without you, I would be stuck in my Beverly Hills apartment laboring over one more spec script that comes "this close" to selling. Without you, I would have thought life in Hollywood was like a 3-D Disney blockbuster—always one more pirate to kick in the teeth before I sailed into the sunset, dancing a jig and singing a hit tune.

But in real life, I would like to acknowledge special people who inspire me: Robert J. Ward (chronically patient husband), Phillip L. Rosen (brilliant entertainment attorney), Alia Yunis (long-time writer friend), Linda Seger (friend and mentor), Kassie Benham (branding diva), Deborrah Hoag (editor-in-chief), Sonja Rocha (graphic designer extraordinare), John E. Simmons (conversion wizard), the late William Kelley (former writing partner and co-conspirator), and Tennessee Williams (former Key West neighbor and my inspiration for writing).

Also, thanks to Cherry Norris, Mark Mower, John Chavez, Carolyn McDonald, Danny Glover, Shane Black, Terry Rossio, Jeremy Piven, Andy Gallerani, Oliver Stone, Babyface Edmonds, Jason Flemyng, Wes Craven, Gary Sinise, John Travolta, Morgan Freeman, Steven Spielberg, Warren Beatty, Jodie Foster, Rob Reiner, Mel Gibson, Dustin Hoffman, Stevie Wonder, Michael Richards, Pierce Brosnan, Bill Pullman, Nicolas Cage, Geena Davis, and Jane Blonde.

Contents

Chapter One
THE PRICE OF INSOMNIA 1

Chapter Two
MOCHA BUZZ. 17

Chapter Three
TRUTH OR CONSEQUENCES 39

Chapter Four
WHOSE STORY IS IT?. 57

Chapter Five
THE LATE ESCAPE 75

Chapter Six
WHAT'S ONE MORE HOSTAGE?. 93

Chapter Seven
ON A MISSION 117

Chapter Eight
GETTING TO THE A-LIST. 137

Chapter Nine
INCOMING ELEMENTS 159

Chapter Ten
THE MORE THE HAIRIER. 179

Chapter Eleven
LET'S GET OUTTA HERE! 197

Chapter Twelve
THE OBLIGATORY CAR CHASE. 217

Chapter Thirteen
CREATING HEAT 237

Chapter Fourteen
WHAT'S THE BIG DEAL?. 257

Chapter Fifteen
SLAMMER 90210 275

Chapter Sixteen
SAPPY ENDINGS 299

FALSE CONFESSIONS

OF A

TRUE HOLLYWOOD SCREENWRITER

Chapter One

THE PRICE OF INSOMNIA

Florida. Present.

I couldn't sleep, so I decided to take my agents hostage.

After all, my chronic insomnia began with their e-mail two weeks earlier: "We think you should find new representation because the timing's not good now."

What did that mean, *The timing's not good now*?

I was a screenwriting client at the Nevison Agency, one of the mid-level literary and talent agencies in Beverly Hills. It was a prestigious company with thirty or so agents. I'd been repped at two of the largest agencies in town and preferred the extra attention of my two Nevison agents, David, the senior agent, and Jason, the junior one. At least until now.

Their bewildering e-mail brush-off came right after Nevison had sent out a script I'd written called *Jane Blonde*. Everyone was certain it would sell. It didn't. My agents said they would get the script to bankable actresses. They didn't.

The right actress could change a pass at the studio into a greenlight. It's a common thing to package a project and attach actresses or directors who could get the movie made. When I asked David about who'd received *Jane Blonde*, he changed the subject.

Jane Blonde was supposed to be my ticket to the A-List. It was high concept, funny and featured the main female character, a 20-something super spy babe, kicking butt but never missing her spa day. Maybe it didn't sell immediately because the budget was too big. Maybe it was because it needed a huge actress to open the movie. Maybe it was because the day it went out to production companies, Mercury was in retrograde.

When my agents avoided discussing the script, I knew this meant that *Jane Blonde* had been overtaken by the hot project of the moment and run off the movie fast- track into the canyon of would-have-been blockbusters. I knew that even though my agents had peed their pants the first time I pitched the story to them, the script now had been erased from the big-commission-coming-soon databases in their tiny brains.

That wasn't the only thing.

Just before the *Jane Blonde* script went out on wide release to production companies and then to the studios, I'd had a meeting with a film producer at Fox Studios who was considering me for a writing assignment. The meeting went well and it looked like I would get the job.

I needed that job.

I asked David and Jason to send one of my scripts to the producer as a writing sample. But the dirty bastards pitched their hot new writing team of Matson & Abner instead, and they got my assignment.

Screw Hollywood.

I was mad as hell and I wasn't going to take this abuse anymore. One thing I'd caught onto early in life: Never, ever be a victim.

I was the child of a single mother who'd left her alcoholic husband when he started smashing her face on Saturday nights. Later I discovered to my great relief, that her ex-husband had not been my biological father. I could have used these excuses and other things to become a weak woman with needles and bottles for friends, but ever since I can remember this voice has been inside me, whispering directions to the Land of Oz. I could see the Yellow Brick Road clearly, and I was determined to skip through any haunted forest wearing those ruby slippers on my way to enlightenment. Be damned, the flying monkeys.

I couldn't let my agents treat me this way. I had to stand up and roar. I had to look them in the eyes and make them tell me the truth. I could handle the truth even if it killed me.

David and Jason probably never expected to hear from me again. After all, I was only an insignificant worker bee in the busy hive of Hollywood and I didn't even live in the hive anymore. I was powerless and persecuted. Right? Wrong.

I had to think outside the circle of confusion. I had to change the timing, right some wrongs and break the rules.

During the eight, long torturous years I'd lived in Los Angeles, which I affectionately call "Hell-A," I longed for an official guide to help unravel the mysteries of show biz. Something like *Hollywood for Dummies*, where I could have read all the rules I had to learn the painful way.

Little did I know, I was writing the book by stumbling from one embarrassing incident to another. It was the book of unspoken rules of the film business and of living in Beverly Hills and Los Angeles County.

Hell-A Rule #1: In Hollywood, there are no rules and they're strictly enforced.

It's a conundrum. There was rarely a clear-cut answer to anything in Hollywood, but I had to know why my agents were dumping me and why my screenwriting career was being swept away in a rip current of indifference.

So I bumbled through sleep deprivation fog to book the next flight from Jacksonville, to Las Vegas, threw a couple of things in my *Mission: Impossible 2* backpack, and laid an incoherent note on the nightstand for my boyfriend, Christopher: *I've gone to Hollywood to fix things. Love, Liz.*

I stood there in the darkness a moment. Eerie silvery moonlight filtered through the sheer drapes on the windows and illuminated Christopher's still face. I watched him sleep. He was a gentleman, even while unconscious. He never snored. Well, he slobbered a bit, but nothing as undignified as snoring. Bless his heart.

The only sounds were the ceiling fan humming overhead and the frogs croaking in the tidal ditch behind the house. I glanced up at a photograph he'd taken in Cannes hanging above the bed, with other arty photos he'd taken on his world travels. That photo always brought me a sense of calm with its stone streets and flowers spilling over ancient walls.

Leaning close to kiss him goodbye, I stopped. If he woke he'd talk me out of my extravagant impulse to storm Beverly Hills, guns blazing. After all, he was the voice of reason in my life. My voice was always that of insanity. That's why I fit so well in Hollywood.

As I backed away from the bed, I had a mournful feeling I may never see Christopher sleeping again.

But if anyone could understand my state of emergency, it was Chris. We met the day I got my first big studio check. It was love at first sight, or something like it. Although it almost was the night we never met.

CUT TO THE PAST:

Beverly Hills.

Our mutual friend, Kira, who thought we were perfect for each other because we were both tall writers, tried to get Christopher and me together on several occasions. Three to be exact. Each time something went askew.

The first was a screening of a Russian film at MGM where Christopher was a no-show. Kira was from Moscow, spoke in a lovely Russian accent and got invited to every movie from her homeland to screen in LA. I hooked up with a cute guy from Georgia —the Georgia in the south of Russia, not the south of America. But when I learned he had a wife and seven children in the Ukraine, we quickly unhooked.

The second time Christopher and I almost met, Kira and I were at the Academy to see the foreign directors talk about their Oscar-nominated films. I had Christopher's ticket and was supposed to meet him in front of the theatre where about 300 people without tickets were lining up, all to see the rage of Hollywood that year: Roberto Benigni. I never saw him, Christopher that is. Roberto was charming. Kira later told me Christopher had been waiting in the line of the ticketless masses. Duh.

So by the third appointed time of our meeting, I was over him.

When Kira called to ask why I wasn't at the Women in Film mixer at The Stinking Rose Garlic Cafe, I told her I had an important deadline involving Oreo cookies. Kira said Christopher was at the mixer at that very moment, and she would never speak to me again if I didn't get my skinny butt down there.

I begrudgingly threw on my leopard-print skirt and black stretchy top and squeezed into my strappy high heels that boosted my normal five-foot-ten-inch height to over six feet. When I finished smearing makeup on, a portentous wave of emotion washed over me. I had an odd feeling life was about to change.

Checking my love-at-first-sight potential at the full-length mirror in my bedroom, I adjusted my skirt that was on crooked. At that moment I was glad I exercised on my stair-stepper every morning to the live car chase on TV. I was trim with just enough hips and ample rear end to strut. I turned sideways and stood up straight, sucking in what little gut I had. I ran a hand over my tummy to smooth out the fabric in my skirt. Not bad.

By coincidence I had just gone to Westside Pavilion to have my hair styled the day before, so the blond highlights on my ash brown hair looked punky and spiked up in a chaotic halo around my face.

Thank God I'd just gotten over my semi-annual bout with hateful zits, and my foundation concealed the aftermath. The overall package was almost glamorous in a tomboyish way.

My Norfolk terrier, Aggie, was barking and throwing her squeaky ball to me enticing me to play. She did this when she saw signs that I was getting ready to leave. She was irresistible with her short legs, pigeon-toed front paws, a little docked tail and blondish red coloring. She looked more like a stuffed animal than a real dog and got a lot of attention from strangers on the sidewalks of Beverly Hills.

I gave Aggie a goodbye bone, jumped in my old Saab and roared down Wilshire to meet my destiny.

There was a total traffic jam on La Cienega, and the Stinking Rose parking lot was full and closed. My car was running on empty. I crashed one of the restaurant lots across the street and headed to the mixer.

Kira was at the front door waiting. "You will love him!" she said in her cute Russian accent.

We made our way through shoulder-to-shoulder slut-babes who were all in search of a star on Hollywood Boulevard. They were all dressed the same.

Hell-A Rule #2: Always wear black or white. You can also get away with funereal colors that appear black, like navy or dark burgundy. No happy colors like red, yellow or bright blue. And never, ever wear pastels. If you look like an Easter egg, you'll end up with egg on your face.

I was determined to hate Christopher, have one drink, then return to my comfy couch with Oreos on the side.

But I didn't have a chance. There was Christopher, all 6'5" of him, towering over everyone in the room. And in a room of 500 beautiful, silicon-injected wannabe actresses, who was he talking to? The only short, bald man within a 10-mile radius.

Christopher's gravitational pull was impossible to resist.

I extended my hand. "*Liz Bradbury,*" I shouted, hoping he could hear me over the cacophony of lies being told in the room.

Christopher's voice was low and Cary Grant-ish with a distinct New Zealand accent. He spoke his name, and although I barely heard it, I knew it already from gossiping with Kira about him. Was he dating anyone in LA? Was he connected to a girlfriend back home in Auckland? Was he secretly gay, and would break my heart in six months?

He had wavy brown hair, a handsome European face, and a warm smile. I chose to overlook the fact that his parents should have insisted on braces during his rebellious teenage years, leaving a confusion of teeth in plain view. That could be fixed.

His eyes were baby blue and told much about him. He was almost shy, but never looked away. His gaze brought a calmness to me. A comfortable levitation of my heart suspended in breathless anticipation of what was to come.

As the freelance Hollywood correspondent for the *New Zealand Herald,*

Christopher interviewed movie stars and directors to write feature articles about new movies being released. It was a glamorous job, although it didn't pay much. One of the first things Christopher said to me was that he wasn't a wealthy man. That was a brilliant way to ferret out the gold diggers and clarify motivations.

After hanging out at the Stinking Rose for enough time to go deaf, Kira invited us to a Russian restaurant where she was hosting a birthday party for her niece. During our dinner, Christopher asked if I liked Lyle Lovett. Even though I only knew one thing about him — he was the music geek married to Julia Roberts at the time — I said, "I love Lyle Lovett."

Christopher invited me to go with him to a Lovett concert that was five months in the future. I was dumbfounded. I'd never had a man I'd known for less than three hours suggest that we plan a date 150 days in advance. He must have really, really liked me.

Within a week, the "M" word came up, and I don't mean murder.

It started out as just a joke on my part that turned into a giddy conversation. On our second date, Christopher asked me to come to his apartment in West Hollywood for dinner. This was even before I had cooked for him, which was a first for this chick.

Christopher's apartment was small and on the third floor of an old apartment complex just south of Sunset Boulevard. The window air conditioner roared in a high- pitched hum, but couldn't keep up with the unusually hot weather. I dabbed at the sweat dripping down my neck and hoped Christopher wouldn't notice.

Dinner was a cool salad with a chilled New Zealand sauvignon blanc.

Over dessert, he poured his heart out to me about his past romantic history. It was a touching tale of one man's quest for true love that had ended in a ten-year relationship with a Kiwi woman who he said refused to marry him or even acknowledge they were domestic partners to her friends. He said she was a feminist. I said she was an idiot.

Even the woman's brother was in a long-term relationship with the mother of his children, yet no wedding in sight. That's how the topic of marriage bubbled to the top of our innocent little chat.

"So do New Zealanders not believe in marriage?" I asked Christopher, wiping perspiration off a brow, hoping it wouldn't smudge my eyebrow pencil.

"Sure we do. Would you like to?" Christopher said as he took a bite of his store-bought chocolate torte.

Was he asking me to marry him? Or was this a hypothetical question? I didn't know, so I said, "Marriage is a good thing with the right person."

"Am I the right person?"

Without thinking, without analyzing or giving myself time to freak out, I said, "Yes."

There was no hesitation, no fear, no doubt.

Six months later, we met 50 jubilant friends and family members in Florida at a restored southern estate house for our wedding.

Christopher's mum and sister came from New Zealand for the big event and my family fortunately welcomed them with open hearts.

Things could have gone differently. The first thing my mother asked about Christopher when I called her from LA was, "Is he white?"

My mother had never heard of New Zealand, and it sounded an awful lot like one of the other "New's." She didn't know where New Guinea or New Delhi was, but she had seen pictures of their residents on CNN, and they didn't look like us.

I grew up colorblind, or maybe it was just that I was a rebel since birth. I liked to think of myself as a Southern Belle with a Rebel yell.

If my family didn't associate with a certain person because their skin wasn't exactly our color or their accent wasn't sufficiently Dixieland, I made a point of bringing that person home for dinner. I made the argument that we were all God's people and besides, what color is a soul? That shut them up.

I would've fallen in love with Christopher, even if his skin had been polka-dotted. We were the perfect match, and on that hot fall day in Florida we were going to make it legal.

As Christopher and I greeted friends in the Victorian Room overlooking a little duck pond in the mansion gardens where we were to wed, I fought to keep my equilibrium and stay upright. No, I had not been sampling the bubbly. My brain was drunk with joy.

After everyone was seated in the garden, I stood with my uncle alone in the Victorian Room, gazing out the French doors that opened down the aisle leading to the man who was to be my husband.

I could see Christopher there with the minister. He was standing in the sunshine, an aura circling his head like a special effect on a Syfy Channel movie. His black suit looked tailormade for him, his white shirt starched and crisp, with the champagne-colored paisley tie he chose making him look like a distinguished hippie.

Someone swung the French doors open as the wedding march began. There was no orchestra, or even a string quartet, but my mom's boom box blasted the music every southern woman longed to hear.

Christopher turned to see me in my champagne-colored dress from M. Cole at Century City Mall in LA. The bodice was lacy and form-fitting. The skirt was made of shiny silk and was cut higher in the front and longer in the back, creating the impression of a short train. I wore a pink pearl necklace and matching earrings I'd found on sale at Neiman-Marcus.

My hairdresser had created a special design with highlights for the occasion, and I felt like an Academy Award nominee right after the presenter called her name.

My uncle escorted me down the brick pathway to where Christopher waited. Every cell in my body was dancing down that aisle with me. Just as my uncle released my arm and I reached for Christopher's hand, a deafening explosion rocked the wedding party.

Everyone ducked for cover away from the thundering sound. When I looked back at the mansion, flames were shooting out of a hole torn in the roof just past the Victorian Room.

Friends and family leapt from their seats and surged past the duck pond onto the oak-covered grounds away from the house. Staff members and kitchen employees poured out of the Victorian Room door, down the aisle, almost trampling Christopher, the minister and me.

Panic and chaos overtook the day, turning my fairytale wedding into the Nightmare on Oak Street. Shortly the place was swarming with sweaty firemen and noisy fire trucks. No one was hurt but the mansion burned to the ground and our nuptials were postponed.

Christopher's mum and sister returned to New Zealand, the mansion declared that the gas explosion in the kitchen was an act of God and refused to refund our $10,000. We sued them, but the former owners fled to Canada to start a chain of southern-fried gator tail fast food restaurants.

We had to save up for a second attempt at tying the knot. So a year went by before we set another wedding date. This time my mom helped us plan everything, since we by then lived in Florida about an hour away from her. We chose a place on the St. Johns River in the middle of downtown Jacksonville for the ceremony and after-party. I had to crash diet to fit into my M. Cole wedding dress. All the details were arranged, guests invited and original wedding rings retrieved from the safe deposit box.

Christopher's mum and sister flew in from New Zealand again, hoping for the best.

Our two families went out with Christopher and me for a joyous, champagne brunch the day before the wedding. Then Christopher went off to play rugby with his mates. I usually went to his matches, but that day I had too many bridely things to do.

I was with all the ladies for a last-minute shopping trip when I got a cell call. It was one of Christopher's teammates, saying Christopher had been injured and that I needed to come to Beaches Hospital.

As Christopher's sister drove us all to the hospital, my imagination ran circles around my rational self. What if Christopher were paralyzed and I would have to take care of an invalid the rest of his life? What if he were on life-support when I got there?

Then my mind reeled back in the opposite direction. It was probably only a broken finger. Or a flesh wound. Why didn't I ask his friend who called what had happened? I just freaked, in turn freaking out all those around me. The entire hysterical party headed for the hospital.

When we got to Christopher's side, he was drifting in and out of consciousness. He had a concussion from a rugby tackle gone wrong. He stayed in that semiconscious state for two days. I never left his room. Christopher's family was there from the beginning of visiting hours until the end. Our mums brought me meals from the hospital cafeteria to keep me going. The third day, Christopher snapped out of it, got out of bed and said it was time to go home.

We missed the wedding again. Christopher said it was a sign, that fate was trying to tell us something. Maybe it was unlucky for us to marry.

He insisted he loved me and definitely wanted to get married if only destiny would cooperate. I assured him we would when the time was right.

The last four years have mostly been marital bliss, sans the marriage. We've lived together as passionate lovers and equal partners in life, and I know Christopher is the perfect man for me. One who lets me think I'm the one who's running the show. Well, sometimes he lets me think that and sometimes I really am. Like when I left the note and flew to Vegas.

BACK TO THE PRESENT:

Las Vegas.

No, my agents who I had come to hate so dearly weren't in Sin City. But Al, a longtime friend, lived there. He was a former employee of a certain department of our government that did nasty things while no one was looking. He had a private store of weapons he used for current mercenary enterprises and I had a feeling I might need a few of them.

I had called him from the Vegas airport, and luckily he was home. Al was a man who took surprises as everyday occurrences. It was like he had been expecting me and said he'd pick me up at the airport. No problem.

The drive to Al's house was always entertaining. There was the view of Vegas' garish casinos from the expressway and, of course, there were Al's wild stories. I never figured out if he was a compulsive liar or one of the most interesting men in my life. He'd said he'd flown for Air America and still hauled cargo for some secret organization. I wasn't sure if it was an official/unofficial black ops unit or some soldier-of-misfortune outfit.

When we got to his house, he had to unlock four locks to get in the front door. The place smelled of gun oil and stale cigarettes.

"You've taken up smoking, Al?" I asked.

"No. Just some of the guys over last night," Al swept papers from a kitchen counter into a stained canvas bag. The stains looked like dried blood.

"Football game?"

"No. We're working on a thing."

I picked up a map of a foreign country that had fallen to the floor. Before I could identify the location, Al confiscated the map.

When he said he had a "thing," Al's friends knew the questions and answers stopped there.

Al sat down on an overstuffed recliner and said, "I'll be gone two weeks. You can use the house."

"Thanks, but I'm headed to LA right now, and I was hoping you could hook me up with something for self defense."

Al smiled, got up out of the recliner and headed upstairs. I followed.

On the second floor, Al unlocked four more locks on a door and swung it open. He turned on an overhead light revealing stained green carpeting. I swear the stains looked like dried blood. There were wall-to-wall bookcases, but in Al's library, there were no books, only guns.

After giving me a tour of his private gun store, Al queried me on my operation. He heard my sketchy plan about taking my agents hostage, as if friends stopped by on a daily basis to pick up weapons for crime sprees. He nodded.

"You know that's illegal, right?"

I gave him a look.

"You'll need a better plan, but here are a few things that will help the execution."

"Execution? You don't think I…oh, you mean execution of a better plan. Cool."

He grinned and loaded me down with armaments.

Al encouraged me to try a little target practice with the big guns, but I was in a bit of a hurry. I had shot all manner of exotic guns for fun with him on a range when he lived in Florida. Besides, paintball with my redneck friends on the Fields of Honor, our game grounds back home, provided plenty of additional training. I wasn't planning on shooting anyone with a real gun in real life. I just wanted to scare them into action.

I rented a subcompact and picked up a nice selection of C-4 plastique, grenades, flame throwers, a few pistols, ammo and a Ruger MP-9. Al said the MP-9 was designed by Uzi Gal, the guy who thought up the Uzi submachine gun. Like the Uzi, the MP-9 fired 600 rounds per minute. Or was it 600 rounds per second? Its magazine held enough 9mm bullets to get the attention of even the most jaded Hollywood player.

Only thing was, the weight of all those arms in the trunk created sparks from the back bumper dragging the asphalt, making me look suspiciously like a drug runner on a budget. So I traded the teeny, tiny car for a Dodge Ram truck and took off for Beverly Hills.

Chapter Two

MOCHA BUZZ

Beverly Hills, Present.

I loved the smell of revenge in the morning. In my manic state, I imagined the best outcome for my mission. My agents would see the light, and Jane Blonde would soon be coming to a theatre near you.

But then a wave of paranoia swept over me as I cruised Rodeo Drive trying to focus on a battle plan. Two weeks' worth of insomnia suddenly created a halo of fatigue and pessimism, so my cerebral cortex just floated there inside my skull in a state of lethargy.

When I first moved to LA, I had planned to stay only a year to get started in the screenwriting business, sign with a literary agency, meet all the right people and hightail it back to my family and friends. But I ended up serving eight years in the Hollywood penitentiary.

I can say with all certainty, had I known I would have to live in that stressed-out, traffic-jammed, pretentious hell-hole called City of Angels for that many years of my life to get to where I am today, I would have said, "No problem."

Things are always worse than you think they'll be, and some things are better left for clairvoyants and madwomen.

CUT TO THE PAST:

Beverly Hills.

"Culture shock" couldn't describe what I suffered in the first few months in Tinseltown. I would prefer to be thrown overboard behind a fishing boat chumming for sharks rather than live through initiation days again. All those promises broken. All those dollars wasted. And that was just the valet parking.

My first encounter with a red-vested valet was at a convenience store. Back home, you drive up at the 7-11, get out, get your six-pack, get back in and pop the top. Simple.

Nothing was that easy in Beverly Hills. The first night I was in my new apartment, I dashed out to pick up cleaning supplies to prepare for the movers arriving the next morning. I saw the convenience store, made a turn into the parking lot, and started to head for a parking space. But suddenly a burly guy wearing a red vest dove off the sidewalk and accosted me. My reflexes reflexed. But before I could gun the accelerator, the guy jerked my car door open.

Oh my God. I'm being carjacked. Perfect. My first night in my new home and mayhem's knocking on my door.

"Welcome to Quik Stop. I'm Hunter. I will be your valet."

I sat there dumbfounded a moment. Then I saw a sign: "VALET PARK-ING $3.50."

I slammed my car door and sped away. I may be delirious but I'm not stupid. And I wasn't paying $3.50 to park at 7-11.

As I raced down Olympic Boulevard, I had a head-on collision with reality: I wasn't in Florida anymore.

BACK TO THE PRESENT:

Beverly Hills.

When I had lived in Beverly Hills, I used to get high from driving down the streets of the Golden Triangle, as the Chamber of Commerce calls it. It's really just the main shopping district of B.H. (Beverly Hills). People disappear in the Bermuda Triangle. Money disappears in the Golden Triangle. World-famous shops and boutiques line the streets: Gucci, Armani, Christian Dior, Ralph Lauren, Valentino, Cartier, Tiffany, Yves Saint Laurent, Coco Chanel, I. Magnin, and Neiman Marcus. Also, there's the insanely expensive Bijan, where you can't just walk in with your platnium card — you must make an appointment.

My pickup was new, but since I was sure every Beverly Hills cop I saw could read my mind and telepathically know my special ops plan, I looked for a city parking garage. One of the reasons shopping was a pleasure in the Golden Triangle was that the city fathers had built an ample supply of parking garages discreetly tucked away between the shops. As you walked along the sidewalk, suddenly there would be glass doors framed in brass with the tasteful seal of the City of Beverly Hills levitating about eye level and bearing the word: PARKING.

There was one time of day to forget about finding a parking space in the garages, and that was 1 to 3 p.m. Lunch. Everyone came to B.H. for lunch meetings, and "FULL" signs blocked all parking garage entrances by 1:05 p.m.

I had hundreds of lunch meetings in the Golden Triangle during my Hollywood incarceration and I soon learned to arrive at 12:30 p.m. for my 1:00 meetings. That way I could calmly find a parking space, have a non-panicked walk to the restaurant du jour and then hide in the shop next door until I saw my lunch partner rushing to the café looking for me. I would then breeze in right behind her or him, calm as a cucumber, looking like I just stepped out of the ending of a feminine hygiene commercial.

The garage on Crescent Drive was where I usually parked when I visited my agents, so I drove around to the garage entrance. Since it was before 1:00, there was plenty of room for stashing my revenge-mobile.

As I backed the truck into a space, I remembered that it wasn't only the convenience of the garages that drew me to them. It was also a tried and true technique to avoid nasty parking tickets. One minute before your parking meter expired in Beverly Hills, a meter maid arrived with electronic ticket writer in hand, and the second the digital timer flashed 0000, a neatly printed parking fine for $135 was under your windshield wiper.

One of the coolest things about having lived in LA for so long was that I knew where everything was. I knew where the exit to the street in this parking garage was. I knew which streets to walk down without a map. I knew which neighborhoods to avoid after sunset.

I made it out onto Crescent and headed south to Wilshire. Then I took a right toward Rodeo.

Walking down Wilshire, I passed the real estate office where 10 years earlier I had signed the lease on my LA apartment. I glanced in the window and saw the Israeli leasing agent who had been delighted to empty my bank account in exchange for a real Beverly Hills address. Today he was chatting away on the phone, waving his hands in the air, laughing and selling another overpriced abode to another underpaid writer, no doubt.

I stood there a moment, transfixed by the memory of how I felt that day, signing that lease, committing to 12 months of living the life of a film writer, or so I hoped.

CUT TO THE PAST:

Beverly Hills.

I was giddy with delirious optimism as I walked out of that office and back to my old Saab. I was overjoyed to get an apartment since I had been sleeping on a bunk bed at my cousin's house in an LA suburb, getting little sleep my first three nights in California. My clothes were wrinkled and disheveled because I only wore cotton, and my cousin's wife had thrown their iron into their pool after going on laundry strike. My hair was adjusting to zero humidity by splitting on the ends and piling up like a haystack.

As I strolled along, imagining hosting intimate dinners with movie stars in my new digs, attending the Academy Awards with a famous director and praying I wouldn't become a victim of the broken-dream syndrome, I noticed something falling from the sky — and it wasn't manna from the studios.

It was a grayish, snow-like substance, but it didn't melt when it drifted to earth. It smelled remotely familiar, almost like barbecue on a warm Fourth of July.

A woman came out of Tiffany's dressed in a sweet little Armani number with the biggest pearls around her neck I'd ever seen outside Woolworth's costume jewelry case. Her gray hair was streaked with charcoal highlights, and her skin glowed from a recent facial.

When the woman noticed the gray matter floating to the ground, she stopped and looked west down Wilshire Boulevard. She stood there a moment, shading her eyes. The expression on her face made me turn to see what she was watching.

It was the Malibu fire. Smoke plumed off the mountains in the distance. The wind carried ash from the burning multimillion-dollar mansions and distributed it throughout the LA metropolitan area.

It was a democratic disaster. The fire took no notice of "No Trespassing" signs on the wrought iron gates along the cliffs overlooking the sparkling Pacific.

Everyone got to touch the only thing that remained of physical possessions belonging to some of the world's most wealthy and famous. Custom-built homes, artwork, designer interiors, priceless photos of private moments of movie stars and past secrets — all transformed to ash on the wind.

The woman in the pearls watched the spectacle a moment and then gracefully removed her cell phone from her $2000 Prada bag. I couldn't take my eyes off the fire and overheard the woman making a call.

"Dear, I think the house is on fire," the woman said coolly. Then there was a short pause and she continued, "The house in Malibu. I think we should just go to Palm Springs." Someone on the other end of the call talked a moment. Then the woman said, "We can cancel when we get to the desert." She returned her cell back to her bag, pulled out a $5 bill, put it in my hand and said, "God bless you, dear."

It was only then that I realized I must have looked like I lived on the street. I had to find an iron and hair stylist. I had never depended on the kindness of strangers, but I wasn't turning down a free $5 bill.

The woman took one more look at her house burning on the horizon and then strutted to a waiting limo.

I wondered who she was. Maybe the wife of a producer I wanted to sell a screenplay to. Maybe the mother of a well-known actor whom I would meet in the future and whose interest would get my first movie made. Maybe a madam to the stars who would get caught up in some sex scandal the next week.

Whoever she was, I was certain of one thing: the woman had enough money and insurance to not give a rat's ass that her 15,000 square foot cottage-by-the-sea was burning to the ground while she shopped. I hoped to be in her ranks soon.

When I got to my car, I could see it was covered with the gray stuff. I wiped an index finger across the windshield and had a look. I wondered whose ash this was and what it had been before the flames swept in.

And then I realized that there was something biblical about the scenario. Something out of the Book of Revelation. Maybe it was a sign that was telling me to run for my life. Or maybe it was a simple message: Welcome to Hell-A.

Whatever the meaning, I couldn't say I hadn't been warned.

Lake Charles, Louisiana.

Moving to LA was the bravest or stupidest thing I'd ever done. I recalled making the trip west on I-10 from Florida. At the end of the first day of bat-out-of-hell driving, I was in bayou country. That was 600 miles in one day.

That first driving day, weird things kept happening around me on the road. Speeding over one marshland bridge, the wheel of another car behind me passed inches from my car headed straight down the left lane toward New Orleans.

An hour later, I saw a station wagon skid off the two-lane highway on the opposite side of the median. It slid sideways into the muddy grass, spun around, flew back up onto I-10 and merged into traffic, still headed east.

Then just before sunset and a mandatory stop for sleep, I had an exhilarating hallucination: Instead of being inside the car driving, I was flying along outside the car above the hood, wind in my face and everything.

It was like I was speeding down the road to hell going 200 miles per hour. I had to stop for some REM.

I pulled off at the next exit, found a hotel, registered and smuggled my puppy into the room. Then I immediately called my mother.

My mom wasn't crazy about the idea of my moving to LA. She'd seen every episode of "LA Law" and knew I'd be murdered as soon as I stepped out of the car. But to her credit, she supported my mad decision to plunge head first into the septic tank of Hollywood. I think some of her support came from the knowledge that just before I left Florida, my mercenary friend, Al, helped me pick out a cute little Ruger .38 pistol that I intended to keep beside the bed, so when the rapists broke in I could defend my honor.

I dialed the number where Mother had lived since I was in second grade. She picked up after the first ring. I didn't even get to say where I was when she shrieked, "You have to come back. LA's on fire!"

My mother was a level-headed woman and not prone to panic, but the alarm in her voice freaked me out.

"Turn on CNN," she insisted.

I grabbed the remote control, found CNN and saw a horrible, horrible sight: LA on fire. A graphic popped up with a ring of fire around a map of metropolitan Los Angeles. Then a live report from Malibu flashed on the screen. A firestorm raced up the hill behind the red-faced reporter toward mansions of the rich and vulnerable.

My Hollywood dreams were going up in flames right there in that Lake Charles hotel room. I sat down on the bed.

"Liz? Do you see it? Everything's on fire," my mom said.

"Yeah. I see it. Everything's on fire."

"Come home, honey. You can write your scripts here, can't you?"

"Sure. But to sell the scripts, I have to be there."

Even though the City of Angels looked like Hades, I was determined to make it through that ring of fire and become a true Hollywood screenwriter. My whole life had led up to that moment and I wasn't wimping out now. It was my calling, my path, my albatross.

Los Angeles.

When I arrived in Southern California Halloween night, I could see the fires as I crept into the LA suburb of Garden Grove on the 91 Freeway. I was headed to my cousin's home for safe shelter while I looked for an apartment.

The CNN graphic got it right: fires circled LA. There were even flames burning down the side of a hill almost to the asphalt of the freeway I was on. It was mesmerizing. The orange-red flames and black smoke disappeared into the sunset. Motorists passed by hardly noticing the fiery menace a few feet away.

Maybe this was a sign. Maybe Mother was right. I should go home. This was no place for a good, sensitive soul. I thought about that for 10 seconds and then my ambition overtook my fear.

BACK TO THE PRESENT:

Beverly Hills.

I headed down the flower-lined sidewalk to find the hottest new scene restaurant in Beverly Hills, NZ. The coolest restaurants and bars in LA used symbols, letters or numbers for their names. Ordinary words or names was, well, ordinary. If I were going to be arrested soon and sent to the Big House, I wanted my last lunch as a free screenwriter to be on bone china in a restaurant with letters for a name.

I saw a woman approaching who looked like a homeless movie star I used to see on the Third Street Promenade in Santa Monica. I could never think of her name. There were so many people like her in LA that there was a special census category to record their numbers: UTBF (Used To Be Famous).

Every time I saw her, I put a dollar in her hand and said, "I love your work."

This never failed to cheer her up. She always asked the same thing: "Are you a producer?"

I always answered the same thing: "No, a writer."

She would get this look on her face, like she smelled dead possum, then walk away.

The homeless actress saw me coming and crossed the street.

By the time I found NZ, I thought I had a decent strategy worked out for my mission. Since everyone in Hollywood took lunch at 1:00 and never returned to their office until after 3:00, I would have lunch at NZ at 1:00. Then I would begin a shopping spree on Rodeo at 2:00 that would last until my credit cards maxed out. After that I would head to Nevison, where I would go out in a blaze of glory or become famous for doing what every screenwriter and actor fantasized about doing — putting a gun to their agent's head and saying, "Do what you promised to do when I signed with your frickin' agency, you sack-o'-shit worm pig."

It was a perfect plan except that I couldn't get a table at NZ. A thought flashed through my cortex. I wondered if the MP-9 would convince them to treat me like bankable talent.

I resisted going back to the truck to get my designer weapons collection. A show of deadly force might get a table with a view of the fountain, but I chose instead to save the drama for the Nevison boys.

So I shuffled down to California Pizza Kitchen, or CPK as it's known to the hipsters. Okay, so it wasn't NZ, but I used to love the barbecue chicken salad there.

When I lived in LA, I missed real southern truck stop cooking and on occasion would bake buttermilk biscuits from my great grandma's recipe. I once tried to make gumbo, but finding fresh okra in Los Angeles was like trying to find handmade tortillas in Northeast Florida.

Hell-A Rule #3: Never ask for okra in a Beverly Hills grocery store. You will be escorted to the nearest Greyhound Bus station, where you will be placed on the next bus back to Hicksville.

Even though I kept my cast-iron skillet on top of the stove for show, I was like everyone else in LA, eating out five nights a week when I could afford it.

Because I moved from the slums of Beverly Hills back to my home state of Florida about a year ago, I hadn't had CPK's barbecue chicken salad for a while, so I worked up a craving for it as I walked down to Beverly Drive.

But CPK was lousy with Young Turks from the William Morris Agency. There was a 45-minute wait, so I had to obliterate the chicken salad from my mind. As I was leaving, I remembered that CPK wasn't one of my favorite places for lunch because lip-reading wasn't a skill I had learned. And reading lips was the only way to understand what your lunch partner, sitting two feet from your face, was saying. The decibel level in the place exceeded the city's noise ordinance. But who cared when they were making million-dollar movie deals?

I crossed the street to Chin Chin, which had Chinese chicken salad to kill for. After waiting for 15 minutes in a mob desperate for dim sum and fame, I found out there was an hour's wait for a seat. I felt like I did almost every day I lived in Hell-A: dejected, downtrodden and defiant.

Fighting my way out the front door, I came to the sidewalk where I'd walked a hundred times. My head automatically turned south toward my old neighborhood. I saw a comforting sight: the sign for one of my old coffeehouse haunts halfway down the block.

I ended up having an ice blended mocha at Coffee Bean and hoped the sugar rush and caffeine would lift my spirits. It did. I swear they put something illegal in those 12 ounces of heaven. Something addictive and wonderful. Something that causes an instant state of euphoria. Sort of like Coke when it first started in the early 1800s, or was it 1900s, putting cocaine in its soda. The fog of insomnia evaporated.

Checking my watch, I knew I had time for a bit of recreational shopping, something I did little of when I lived in Beverly Hills due to the recreational stress of I receiving my credit card bills.

Walking to Wilshire on Beverly always induced flashbacks, primarily because the office building on the southeast corner of Beverly and Wilshire housed the first agent I delivered a script package to after I moved to California. He needed clients. I needed an agent. A year after I delivered that package, the agent decided on an easier career path — professional tennis. Maybe I should have done the same.

It had been years since I delivered that first package to an agent. But anytime I went near that building, I got that same wildly optimistic rush of unbridled naiveté I felt that day.

That was before I knew that nobody cared that I was a damned good writer with damned good ideas who was willing to work my ass off to make it in Hollywood. Five thousand others just like me had arrived the same week, and we would all have to learn our lesson: It wasn't about the talent. It was about who you knew, or more importantly, who knew you.

Rodeo Drive was thick with tourists. You can always spot them. They dressed up to shop in Beverly Hills: Worthington suits from Penney's, cubic zirconium from the Shopping Channel, and a rip-off Prada bag from Chinatown. Rodeo designer casual was the wardrobe of choice for the real veterans, as they dashed in and out of their limos double-parked in front of Geary's or Armani.

I'd always wanted something from Tiffany's. Something small. Something with my birthstone, which was diamond. Maybe I could find a microscopic pendant for under $1,000. I couldn't remember going into Tiffany's during my service in LA. There was no reason to visit since my monastic budget held me hostage. Browsing would only get my materialistic girl all riled up.

So when I hauled the heavy door open, I was hoping to be happily surprised to find the perfect bauble. But the instant I stepped inside and the door closed behind me, every sales person in the store turned to inspect me. Quickly, they all went back to their more important customers or dusting. It was like I was telepathically communicating: "I have no net worth, so please don't acknowledge that I exist."

I was out of place. I wanted to run away, but managed to stumble to a counter of sparkling diamond necklaces and pretend to browse. A sales associate was standing about two feet away from me. He was dressed in a tailored black suit, expensive white shirt with thin black stripes, and diamond cuff links. He had dark wavy hair and a spectacular tan. Even though he wasn't assisting another customer, he didn't offer to take anything out of the case for me. Did he mistake me for a criminal or low-life?

The salesman turned his back on me to whisper to another sales person, a young woman with a severe charcoal suit on and blond hair swept up in a twist on her pointy head.

The attitude on the hired help made me nauseous, so I fled. When I got outside, I could breathe again. There was something stifling about being close to all that wealth and snobbery.

I gave up on a shopping spree and went back to Coffee Bean for another iced mocha. As I walked to the counter to order, the rich aroma of gourmet coffee wrapped me in a blanket of well-being.

While I waited in line, or in the queue, as Christopher said, my brain was running in hyperspeed. I thought about my man. I wondered why he hadn't called my cell to ask what the hell was going on. Then I remembered my cell was probably off.

I was not one of those automatons that was a slave to text messaging or the buzz of my cell phone. I turned it on only when I wanted to make a call. I let incoming calls go to voicemail, and I rarely checked for messages. It was my futile attempt not to be swept away in the white water of a world gone tech-mad.

I checked missed calls and sure enough, there were ten from Christopher. Just as I was deciding whether to call him, I heard someone say, "May I help you?" I ordered another iced mocha and moved to the next line where other Coffee Bean addicts sweated it out waiting for their fixes.

Okay, maybe I should at least listen to Christopher's voice mail messages. After all, something could have happened to my mother or sister or uncles or aunt. A loved one could be hooked up to a respirator at this very moment, or worse.

I called my voice mail. The messages from Christopher grew more frantic as he tried to reach me again and again, pleading for me to call. But by the tenth, anger ruled. His normally quiet Cary Grant voice became more like Hannibal Lecter on a rant.

He wanted to know why I'd suddenly gone to LA without talking to him. Had I found an e-mail in the middle of the night when I couldn't sleep? Had my agents taken me back and set an important pitch meeting? What could have possibly gotten me on a 6 a.m. flight to the West Coast?

Should I call him? If I did, I couldn't lie to him. He'd try to get me to abandon my mission. He'd ask what I thought I would accomplish by taking my agents hostage. He would point out the consequences: death or imprisonment.

Death or imprisonment. Fine for my characters. Not so fine for me.

I speed-dialed his number at his office where he worked as a newspaper editor and part-time photographer. I got a recording. Hearing his voice made me want to get on the next plane home. After the beep, I couldn't think of anything to say except "I love you." So that's what I said and hung up.

Love means never having to say you're wrong.

But should I reconsider my path here? Should I walk back to the parking garage, enjoying the California sun and LA smog, get in the truck and drive home? Yes, that would be the rational thing to do, the sensible course of action, the safe, chicken-shit cop-out.

As I sipped my second mocha, I noticed a writer with his laptop buzzing, writing the next $5 million spec, no doubt. That was me a few years ago.

Coffee Bean and Starbucks were the official rent-free offices of every writer in town. Each location had at least a dozen regulars drifting in and out each day, fighting for their usual table.

Free-range screenwriters living on Ramen noodles and lattes looking for a break. You could write a little and chat with strangers you hoped would turn out to work for Jerry Bruckheimer or Ron Howard. You could take meetings with indie producers, who would also use the ubiquitous coffee havens as headquarters and bullshit each other about making movies together.

Hell-A Rule #4: Meetings have rankings. You can tell how important you are to the person who invited you by the time and place of your meeting. From least important to most, they are: phone meeting, office meeting, coffee meeting, breakfast meeting, lunch meeting, drinks meeting, dinner meeting.

Hell-A Rule #5: Screenwriters never get dinner meetings unless their new movie just grossed $100 million the weekend before. Then two dinner meetings a night for two weeks is the rule.

Ah, the bad ol' days. I missed them for about 10 seconds, then my mind bounced back to death and imprisonment.

I ran the worst-case scenario over in my brain. What if men in uniforms rushed into the building and shot me? I couldn't remember being shot before, but I had a dream about it once. There was this odd hot pain in my shoulder where the .38 slug entered. I felt warm liquid flowing down my shoulder, coloring my white blouse crimson. A dizzy calm came over me as I sat down on the floor of the mall. That's when I woke up.

I don't know if that's really what it's like, but that was vivid enough for me. I guess it depends on where you get shot. Some places would probably be more troublesome than others. Like a gunshot to the head would be a real bummer.

Death had always intrigued me. Where did one go when the body died? I mean, one second you're speeding along a rain-slicked highway, pitching a story to a producer on the cell phone when a pulpwood truck loses its load. The next second, you're pitching your life story to the man upstairs, hoping to get an office on the lot of Heavenly Studios.

Ever since I was a child I have felt separate from my body. I always knew "I" was more than the flesh that carried my essence on earth. When I was five I told Betsy Bowling, my best friend, that I was from Mars. I believed it then. Maybe thinking I was an alien made me feel special. Or maybe it was that being from another planet meant that I was separate from some of the depraved adults around me who should have been put on a spaceship and blasted into the nearest black hole.

One thing for sure, I can connect to an infinite source and disconnect from my earthly self at will. Maybe it's from years of meditation, maybe it's something else. Like schizophrenia.

So thinking in a logical way about death, I came to the conclusion that it's a natural transition, similar to my daily moments connected to God or the universe or whatever you want to call it, only longer. Much longer. Which is not necessarily a bad thing.

If that's what death of my body will be like, I am not afraid.

By the time I was through my fourth mocha, I had adrenaline pumping through my veins and a plan of attack outlined on a pile of napkins. I numbered them so I wouldn't get the order of events mixed up.

I was feeling invincible. Maybe it was a manic high. But from my comfortable chair at Coffee Bean, the plan looked doable: Meet with my agents, make them confess that they hadn't really sent out the *Jane Blonde* script to the actresses they said they would, take them hostage and make them send out the scripts. Or better yet, we could hand-deliver script packages directly to the actresses. Oh, but what about the police?

If the authorities and press got involved, that was good, because what actress wouldn't read a script that had been the subject of breaking news and continuous live broadcasts on TV? The more I thought about it, the more sense the plan made. Anything famous gets the attention of producers and talent. Everybody would want to say they were signed on for the *Jane Blonde* project after everyone else had heard about it. I was certain the Nevison receptionist would be flooded with incoming calls about reading the script once the live coverage started. Or would the building be evacuated and the phones go to voice mail? I was ready to find out. Full of optimism and caffeine, I headed out to begin my mission.

There was a breeze coming down Beverly as I made my way north. The street was bumper-to-bumper with limos and exotic cars. I could hear horns blowing up on Wilshire, meaning that the traffic jams were already blocking intersections and incidents of road rage were imminent. I needed to accelerate my kidnapping schedule before the Golden Triangle was gridlocked, and no escape would be possible.

As I came to the corner of Wilshire and Beverly with visions of vengeance dancing in my head, an unexpected encounter almost threw me off-course.

"Liz, what are you doing here?" said a voice that shattered my daydream.

I half-turned toward the voice and saw my long-time friend, Zaida. I squealed and flung my arms around her in an embarrassing public display of friendship.

"Zaida. Wow, it's you!"

I peeled myself off her and she stepped back, giggling. She was yin and I was yang. The force of my personality sometimes sent her for shelter.

Zaida and I met in the Wisconsin Screenwriters Forum, LA chapter shortly after I arrived in town. She had just won the Warner Bros. comedy writing competition. So the studio brought her to LA from Chicago, and she stayed.

We shared a propensity for humor, both in our writing and in our desperate, single-girl lives. We both suffered from mood swings caused by a disorder called poverty. We critiqued each other's scripts and took turns hosting the writers' group. Zaida made Middle Eastern cuisine since her family was from Lebanon, and I did southern tapas: boiled peanuts, fried pork skins and Ritz crackers with Cheese Whiz.

Zaida pushed a lock of silky black hair off her face and said, "Why didn't you tell me you were coming to town?"

"I didn't know. I just hopped on a plane and flew out this morning."

She smiled, looking around since she never maintained eye contact for more than a few seconds. "Oh, so you must have a really important meeting."

I thought about confessing my sinful plan, but decided against it since it would sound too arrogant or delirious.

"Right. Well, I'm just meeting with David and Jason."

"Are you still with them? Weren't you thinking of moving to another agency?"

I checked my watch. I would have to hurry if I were going to catch my agents by surprise before they went to lunch.

Zaida, who was hyper-sensitive to any body language that telegraphed discomfort in her presence said, "Oh, you have a lunch meeting with Jason and David?"

"I really should get on over there."

Zaida tried not to look hurt. "Okay. Well…"

"What are you doing this afternoon?" I asked.

Her expression brightened. "Just procrastinating about this rewrite I'm doing."

"Okay, listen. If you're home, check the TV for breaking news, and I'll try to call you later."

I noticed the signal light was ready to change and dashed across the street, leaving Zaida wondering what the hell I was talking about.

When I got to the rental truck I found a parking ticket on the windshield. I'm the only person in the Milky Way galaxy who can park inside a parking garage to avoid a ticket and actually get a citation anyway. The ticket was for violating the "head in only" parking law. How could I forget about that life-or-death regulation?

I'd gotten a citation when I first moved to Beverly Hills for ignoring the "head in" regulation and for not having a license plate on the front of the vehicle. It didn't matter that folks in Florida weren't required to have a front and back tag; when in California you had to do as the Californians do or be ticketed for civil disobedience. Ignorance of the law was no joke.

On this trip I parked in the last space on the basement floor behind a dumpster, hoping the truck wouldn't be found right away. I figured once the siege of the Nevison Agency began, SWAT would be searching for the perp's vehicle and a Nevada license plate would be a certain tip-off. Then they'd find traces of C4 in the truck, then they'd track the tag number to Cheap Skate Car Rentals at the Las Vegas airport, then they'd know it was me, then they'd call my house and call forwarding would ring Christopher's work. And I really preferred that he find out what I did during my summer vacation on CNN.

Parking tickets always pissed me off. This one was no exception, so after I cussed at it, spit on it and ripped it to shreds, I stuffed it in the little envelope that came with it, wrote "Screw the Fascist State" on the back flap, and tossed it in the mail box on the corner.

Having successfully resolved that little irritation, I felt inspired. That was easy. Taking everyone on the second floor of the Nevison Agency hostage would be a snap.

So I went back to the truck to pick up my armaments. That's when I found I'd accidentally left the truck unlocked. And not only that, one of the pistols, the bad-ass

MP-9, was lying in plain sight on the dashboard right at the spot where the parking ticket had been placed so neatly under the wiper.

Was the parking attendant so dazed as not to have seen the weapon? Or were armaments such a common sight in the cityscape as to go unnoticed? Or had they seen it and called 911?

My head snapped around looking for any sign of snipers, SWAT tanks or Gloria Allred. Nothing but a Rolls-Royce cruising for a space. The Rolls stopped, the driver's window glided down and Clint Eastwood said to me, "Go ahead, make my day. Tell me you're leaving."

I swear he said it, just like in *Dirty Harry*. My brain disconnected from reality for a split second in a desperate attempt to determine if this was real life or an alternate movie universe.

"I…I…I…" I sounded like a mariachi recording stuck in a groove.

Before I could say something intelligible, the Rolls squealed its tires racing in reverse for a newly vacant spot.

My mind turned back to righting a wrong. Or maybe it was revenge. What-ever it was, I was a warrior for the little screenwriter. A ninja for the gifted and introverted. Like my girl Jane Blonde, I was on a mission, so get out of my way.

My agent's email said, "the timing's not good now."

I shoved the pistol into my backpack with the other weapons, strapped on my bulletproof vest, shouldered the 50 pounds of armory in the pack and headed around the block to change the timing.

Chapter Three

TRUTH OR CONSEQUENCES

Beverly Hills, Present.

As I came to the shiny faux-gold-leaf door engraved with the Nevison Agency name, I stopped. Did I really want to do this? Could I go through with it once I met with David and Jason? I reasoned that I could always change my mind, up to a point. Once I stepped over the line between contentious meeting and kidnapping plot, there was no turning back.

Suddenly Matson & Abner burst out the doors. They were the writers who'd stolen my Fox Studios writing assignment, thanks to my skanky agents.

They were both wearing the male comedy writer uniform: baseball cap, obscure rock concert tour T-shirt, old jeans and sneakers. They both had homeless person hair created by $75 styling goop from a certain Rodeo Drive salon. That stuff had a unique fragrance. It smelled like sex.

One of the writers carried a distressed-leather laptop computer case with a set of car keys clipped to the handle. A shiny new Lamborghini emblem dangled in plain view. That should have been my Lamborghini.

They almost ran me down, completely oblivious to my presence.

I heard Abner say to Matson, or was it Matson to Abner, "Man, David and

Jason, they're the best. Can you believe they got us $4 million for that piece-of-crap script?"

They were on the top of the A-List. I would be happy with the bottom of the A-List. In reality, I was on Hollywood's F-U List.

You know what I'm thinking. Yeah, I could have blown them away right there, blah, blah, blah. But if I were going through with my plan, that could add insurmountable complications. The whole building would be locked down faster than you could say Hollywood Walk of Shame, and then where would I be? Waiting in the stupid lobby with yesterday's *Variety* and Evian — just like old times, only I'd be waiting to be taken into custody instead of into the conference room.

I stood there a moment, watching Matson and Abner until they disappeared around a corner. I hadn't come this far to back down now. I regained my focus and pulled open the heavy door to the future.

May the force be with me.

I tried to act cool and headed across the polished maple floor toward the receptionist. Yes, I knew where the elevator was and yes, I knew where my agents' offices were. But see, the big agencies have too many disgruntled current clients or homicidal former clients who know where the elevators and offices are to allow unrestricted run of the building. So someone upstairs had to come down to get you with their elevator key card.

At some of the big agencies, and believe me I've been represented by most of them at one time or another, receptionists can give attitude. They may not make enough money to buy a Del Taco bean burrito, but that doesn't stop them from putting on a condescending air. For some reason, the receptionists at Nevison had always been warm folks. I'm not sure why this was, but it was.

Nevison had an understated reception area, not like the grand lobby of CAA with the Lichtenstein painting and marble floors. It was a somewhat warm place for an agency. Only thing was, once you came through the glass doors and made the left turn toward the receptionist, there was zero natural light. There was no window in the waiting area, and it had the feel of a cocktail lounge without the bar.

As I approached, the receptionist looked up and smiled.

"Cool vest," She said sincerely.

I looked down at my gunmetal-gray bulletproof vest. I had to admit it was pretty hip.

"Thanks. It's SWAT," I said, wondering if she would get the lame joke.

She didn't.

"That a New York designer?"

"How did you guess?"

When the receptionist called upstairs, of course my agents were shocked to hear that I was actually, physically in person in the lobby. Just yesterday I was in Florida. How could I possibly be downstairs? Maybe I hadn't been in Florida yesterday or last week. Maybe I hadn't gotten their e-mail about finding other representation. That meant they'd have to tell me face to face, which could be a tad unpleasant for everyone.

As I squirmed on the red leather sofa, my eyes drifted to a painting on the wall. I think it was supposed to be an abstract landscape, but I was certain I could make out tortured, screaming faces like Dante's Inferno. Perfect for greeting the angst-ridden clients of a Hollywood agency. I suddenly remembered the first time I'd seen that painting.

CUT TO THE PAST:

Beverly Hills.

It was the end of my first year I was in LA. I was broke, disillusioned and hopeful that a meeting with a Nevison agent would change my life.

I was learning that if safety was your thing, screenwriting wasn't your game. Transitioning from a generous salary as a magazine editor in Florida to writing screenplays in hopes of selling them was like traversing the Grand Canyon on an invisible bridge.

Hell-A Rule #6: To succeed in the screenwriting business, you have to have more than faith. You have to have more than talent. You must have some family history of mental illness.

The Nevison agent I met with had read a couple of scripts I'd written. We sat upstairs in the conference room, and he gushed about the character development and perfect plot structure of one of the screenplays. He said Nevison was looking for a female feature writer who could crank out action comedy. He said he was a "fan" of my work, but he'd have to talk to the group about me.

Two weeks went by and I didn't hear from him. What could have happened? Maybe the group didn't share his enthusiasm for my writing. I called his office and chit-chatted with his assistant, pretending I was interested in her hometown of Boise, Idaho. I left a message, but my potential new agent never returned my call.

Cruel and unusual. Two essential character traits of a prosperous LA agent. The smell of payback was in the air.

BACK TO THE PRESENT:

Beverly Hills.

After 15 minutes, Jason, the junior agent, came downstairs.

Jason was not so tall and had a runner's body. His hair was a blondish brown. He was always well dressed, although I got the idea his wardrobe was off the sale racks at Nordstrom rather than the men's stores along Rodeo. He had a handsome, exotic look about him. I suspected some branch of his family had lived in Northern Italy at one time.

He usually had a smile for me, but today he greeted me like I was the homeless woman outside NZ. He came into the lobby, extending his hand in a lifeless handshake. He would have normally whisked me toward the elevators by now, but instead stood awkwardly in the lobby.

"So, we're really sorry, but we're slammed right now. There's this big deal we're in the middle of. I mean, we didn't realize you were in town," he said as he watched another agent come out the elevator and leave.

Jason turned back in my direction and continued, "Maybe we could make an appointment for next week."

"Did you get my newest script?" I asked.

He stepped sideways toward the elevator like he wanted to escape. He didn't have the guts to look me in the eyes.

"Did you get our last e-mail?" He asked.

"I've been visiting friends in Vegas and didn't get e-mail while I was there."

"Well, if you just give us a call, maybe tomorrow morning, we can set up something for next week." He turned to go.

"Okay. No problem. I do have a new project you should see. And I was just talking to Clint Eastwood..." I said quietly.

Anytime you lower your voice in Hollywood, anyone within 20 feet amps up their superhero hearing, trying to eavesdrop. So bringing the last few words of my final sentence down to almost a whisper got his attention.

He stopped and looked back, saying, "You mean, Eastwood's people."

"No, I mean Clint Eastwood himself."

That's all I had to say. Certain names function as magic words in Hollywood. Say them, and it's like letting the genie out of the bottle. Your wish is spontaneously granted.

So into the magic elevator we went.

The 20 seconds it took to make it to the second floor were spent in discomfited silence. Jason always stood in a stiff-backed posture with his butt hyperextended which gave the impression he was having a colonoscopy.

There was a constant scowl on his face he tried to hide with a forced smile that made him look like Jack Nicholson as The Joker in *Batman*. I reasoned Jason's tortured physical appearance was due to the fact he was a junior agent being initiated into agentdom. This required time served getting reamed by the senior agent, David, who was rumored to be a descendant of the Marquis de Sade.

Jason installed me in the conference room, where most of our meetings had been, and went to get David.

The Nevison conference room was not overly pretentious. It had two glass walls covered by silvery mini-blinds that were open at the moment. The other two walls were painted in this week's hot new interior design color. Every time I was there, the painted walls were a different "now" color. There was a big video-conferencing screen and conference call speaker-phones in the middle of the massive, shiny table.

I dropped my backpack on the table. The metal of the weaponry clanked on the light blond wood.

Instantly Jason and David's assistant, Tiffany, appeared. She was a chirpy little thing decked out in black Gap jeans, a clingy pink sweater and black and pink stilettos. She wore earrings of clear Swarovski crystals and silver beads. She must have taken a jewelry-making class at that bead shop on Santa Monica. Her jet-black hair was swooped up into a ponytail of dreadlocks. Her pale white skin was oddly translucent like the geckos in Key West.

"Evian, Red Bull or Starbucks?" Tiffany asked in a cartoonish, Betty Boopy voice.

"Can someone get me a Coffee Bean ice-blended mocha, non-fat?"

There was a moment when Tiffy's brain tried to compute whether I was important enough to warrant her time to make the trek to Coffee Bean.

"Let me check."

No agent's assistant ever did anything without the blessing of her boss. So she disappeared for about 30 seconds and then popped back in.

"Did you say non-fat?"

I gave her the thumbs up. She smiled and vanished again.

Surveying the room, I decided it would be best to shut the mini-blinds on the glass walls. When I took hostages I wanted privacy.

So I casually closed the blinds. An assistant, or junior agent or soon-to-be studio president rushing by on the way to his next emergency saw me. He gave me an odd look but couldn't be bothered to investigate.

I checked the conference room door. No lock. Damn.

I dragged one of the plush leather chairs to the door, tilted it up on two legs and jammed the back under the knob. Just as I did this, I saw the knob turning. Before I could dislodge the chair, the door opened an inch until the chair legs digging into the sisal carpeting stopped it.

The door slammed closed. Then just as I moved the chair, the door opened with such force that it knocked me down with the chair on top of me.

I looked up to see David and Jason standing over me, obviously perplexed by the situation.

"Oh, I was just working out a scene," I said, trying to sound convincing.

They looked unsure. I struggled up as gracefully as possible.

"Action thriller about an artist who takes a gallery owner hostage."

"Sounds great," David lied as he headed to the other side of the table, followed by Jason.

I managed to get the chair back to the big shiny table and sat down.

David was movie star handsome. I always wondered if he had come to California to be an actor, but never asked because I didn't want to acknowledge any physical attraction. He had this Tom Cruise/Brad Pitt/Johnny Depp kind of thing going on.

On the surface, he was charming. But inside, he was a vessel of toxic sludge, a noxious cocktail of anger, hate, greed, envy and fear. All prerequisites for becoming a great Hollywood agent.

His eyes gave him away. When he looked at you, it was like he was looking through you, like you weren't really there. It gave me the heebie jeebies.

"We didn't realize you were coming out." David sat across from me. Jason beside him.

"I just decided this morning," I said.

"So, Jason tells me you didn't get our last e-mail."

"Well, I've been..."

Before I could finish the sentence David cut in. "Yeah, Jason told me. So what's this about Clint Eastwood being attached to your new project?"

In Hollywood, each second is worth money and there's no time to waste on pleasantries. I once overheard a development executive at a well-known production company refuse to talk with his dying grandmother on her 90th birthday when she called because he was in the middle of a deal.

"I didn't say Eastwood was attached."

"But you did say Clint Eastwood was interested." David cut his eyes at Jason as if he would have his parking space moved to West Hollywood if he had gotten it wrong.

Suddenly, the conference room door swung open and Tiffany dashed in with the mocha.

"Sorry it took so long," she said, out of lung capacity. "Someone from Morris was there ordering for the whole lit department."

David gave her an unappreciative look that everyone noticed.

Tiffany put the mocha on the table with assorted packages of Sweet 'N Low, Splenda, NutraSweet and Stevia. Then she tip-toed toward the door like she was trying not to disturb a slumbering ogre. She closed the door behind her.

I noticed Jason noticing the closed blinds. I figured I had about 10 seconds.

But, alas, the mocha was too seductive. I realized that I had forgotten to tell Miss Tiffany to hold the whipped cream, so there was a two-inch crown of 500 calories topping the mocha. I used the straw to flick the whipped cream onto the shiny table.

The agents gave each other a look, bewildered by my audacity. I took a long drag on the straw. God, I loved that stuff.

"Well, I've got a conference call with Sony, so why don't you tell Jason about your new project?" David growled as he got up to leave.

"Listen, I need to talk to you about *Jane Blonde*," I said, unfortunately in a pleading voice.

David glared at me and started around the table. I knew he'd be out the door in an instant. I intercepted him.

"I need to know if you sent the script to those actresses you said you would," I said.

I really hoped he would sit down and discuss this in a civil manner. I felt myself chickening out of the whole hostage operation.

But David wouldn't talk to me. He wouldn't look at me. He pushed me aside like someone in his way after a screening. His condescending attitude pissed me off.

I knew if I was going to do this thing it had to be now.

"There's something I want you to see."

David turned to look as I reached into my backpack, feeling for the MP-9.

"If it's a new script, forget about it. We're not your agents anymore," said David.

I grabbed the MP-9 out of the bag and aimed it in David's direction. God, it was a heavy mother.

In the moment that David saw the high-powered, semi-automatic chaos-causer, he froze. His eyes stalled on the barrel where a piece of hot metal could exit in slo-mo any second. A piece of metal that would alter our personal histories.

"Sit down." Those two words came out of my mouth so calmly that I sounded like a character from one of my scripts.

He hesitated a dramatic moment and then he sat down.

That's when I realized that I was in control.

I love that word: control. It's a word that's rarely used in connection with a screenwriter. Unless, of course, they suddenly are an overnight success after struggling for 10 years, and their first picture that gets made grosses $200 million the opening weekend. Then you're offered a three-picture deal at Sony and get to direct the next one. That's about as close to control as you get.

I had it all planned out on those Coffee Bean napkins. Exactly how the scene would go. Every detail. Just like in my scripts, but where were the napkins? I rummaged in the backpack with my free hand. No napkins. No notes. That's when I remembered I must have left them in the truck. Damn Clint Eastwood.

This was worse than going in to pitch to the studio V.P. without pitch notes. There was no choice. I had to improvise. After writing Hollywood three-act structures for so many years, my brain automatically organized everything in life into formulaic scenes, scene sequences and acts including turning points. I could improvise on the fly, couldn't I?

I tried to remember what was on the napkins. It was all plotted out so perfectly, right down to the arrest and media crowd waiting outside on the street. But now my mind was blank. For the first time since I began putting words on paper, I was blocked.

My synapses wouldn't synapse. My brain was drained. My life was over.

I had this terrifying realization I was starting to sound like that crazy Charlie Kaufman. You know, the screenwriter who wrote the wacko indie movie *Being John Malkovich* and then somehow got an assignment to do an adaptation of the book *The Orchid Thief.* Only he couldn't figure out how to write a script about flowers, but he didn't want to give back the 50 percent commencement money, so he wrote a script about not being able to write the adaptation.

I would like to have seen the look on the studio exec's face when he read the first few pages of Kaufman's first draft. It must have looked a lot like the look on my face at that very moment. A look of utter confusion. A look of desperation. A look of opportunity coming into focus.

"Sit down," I said again about the same time I saw that my hostages were already sitting down.

They didn't say anything. Just stared up at me, their irritation building.

Then I remembered the chair. I jammed it under the doorknob just as the door started to open. I slammed it closed. Someone knocked.

I looked over at David and Jason.

David glared up at me and said in a staccato rhythm, "This. Is. Bullshit."

Another knock, then I heard footsteps disappearing down the hall.

David stood up, came toward me and said, "What the hell are you doing?"

"I'm taking control of destiny, changing the timing, righting a wrong." I blabbered, going with the flow of consciousness.

David's nostrils flared. His face became pink as he said, "You're starting to really piss me off now."

"Frankly, my precious, I don't give a damn," I said, combining quotes from two of my favorite books that were made into movies.

I held the MP-9 between us, my left hand wrapped around the base of my right hand, like my weapons consultant, Al, taught me on the shooting range. It looked like I meant business.

In the moment that followed, time stopped. It was like driving in a dense fog and smashing into an invisible wall. Every cell in your body comes to a sudden halt and you think: What just happened?

The phone on the Nevison conference table beeped. Two tiny beeps. The outside world trying to get in. David studied me a moment, then vaulted toward the phone.

These were the kinds of moments I lived for. One of the reasons I brought home a trophy after every autocross race was because my reflexes ran on hyperspeed. It was in my blood.

My real dad was a stock car racer before NASCAR was NASCAR. After he was almost killed racing, he sponsored a race team instead of getting on the track himself. I grew up at the infield of the Daytona Beach International Speedway and started autocross racing with a Jensen Healey, graduating eventually to a Formula-Vee.

Before David's manicured fingers touched the smooth plastic receiver, I had leapt onto the table, slid across the polished wood and unclipped the incoming line.

David was not the kind of guy who enjoyed losing. He stood there ready to implode. "What the hell do you want?"

Jason eased out of his chair. He looked pale, as if he were going to heave. Some time ago I figured out Jason was passive aggressive and knew he would avoid conflict whenever possible. So when I wanted something from Nevison, I called Jason. He never said no, at least not directly.

I hopped off the table with the MP-9 leveled at David's crocodile belt and said, "I want the truth."

David glanced at Jason as if he blamed him for this outrageous situation. I felt sorry for Jason and almost regretted putting him in David's line of fire. He was a nice guy, for an agent, and I knew David would savage him if they survived this incident. He would probably be fired for bringing the Trojan horse through the gates of the fort.

David turned back to me, glaring a moment and then averted his eyes.

"Truth about what?" David asked.

"The truth about *Jane Blonde*," I answered.

CUT TO THE PAST:

Los Angeles.

When I pitched *Jane Blonde* to my entertainment attorney, Zen Man, there was dead silence on the phone, then he said, "This is it. Your ticket. This will change your life."

Zen Man rarely got juiced up about things. That's one of the reasons I chose him to represent me. Another reason is that I believe in fate.

Zen Man taught a class at UCLA about the business and legal side of the film biz. I was among 30 students eager to learn how not to get screwed by Hollywood. I was impressed by his knowledge, centeredness and good looks.

So a couple of months later when I was a panelist during a sold-out screenwriting seminar, and a writer asked how to know whether you're getting a good deal, I answered, "You must take a class at UCLA called Making the Deal. Write it down." All 500 writers in the room made a note.

After the panel was over, attendees swarmed the stage, networking, asking follow-up questions and performing oral sex on panelists to get their attention.

The other panelists, who had more impressive credits than I, had more swarmees and better sex. I had a few eager-eyed writers desperate for answers to the enigmas of Hollywood. As I spewed forth screenwriting truisms I made up on the spot, I noticed a familiar face headed down the aisle toward me.

It was Zen Man.

He was in the audience when I commanded everyone to take his class. He was shocked and awed to hear his own name mentioned, since he had come to the workshop to learn more about screenwriting so he could better serve the writers he represented.

We went out to lunch afterward. I told him about my current attorney who stole one of my projects by optioning the rights to remake a foreign film for himself, rather than for me.

Was I bitter about my former attorney stealing my project? Hell yes, but hey, that was sewage under the bridge. Besides, Don Johnson's company ended up with the film rights after my lawyer allowed the option to expire. If the remake gets to the big screen it'll be a miracle, like every other film that gets made in mainstream Hollywood.

Greed is like dirty air in Hollywood. It's part of the big picture. You have to accept greed as you have to accept the damage to your lungs. Either that, or get the hell out of Tinseltown.

"A greedy man has greed for a lover," Zen Man said as he gulped down his organic tofu lasagna with handpicked basil. Having no idea what he meant, I nodded in agreement.

Zen Man offered to represent me. But first he was off to a Buddhist retreat in the mountains where he and others would not speak for a week. Any attorney who was enlightened enough to keep his mouth shut for seven straight days was my kind of lawyer.

Zen Man had represented some of my projects before *Jane Blonde*, but he really believed *Jane* was The One. So did a young producer Zen Man had introduced me to. He was over at Paramount where he had set up a movie with Mel Gibson's company, Icon, when he answered his cell and I pitched *Jane* to him. He said he'd stop by and pick me up for lunch. Cool.

Beverly Hills.

Shortly after I got into Fireball's SUV I knew we'd make a good team. He was multitasking — looking up something in his GPS, talking on his hands-free cell, and weaving through traffic on Santa Monica. His driving skills were on par with fastest-time-of-day autocross champs or NASCAR stars. I called him Fireball after Fireball Roberts, my dad's legendary NASCAR driver. The moniker also related to his career that was taking off like a fireball out of hell. I intended to hang on for the ride.

We had pasta at Il Fornaio on Beverly Drive where we spotted Michael Richards without his Fright Night weave. Richards was handsome and even sexy sans the Kramer antics. Then I noticed Pierce Brosnan with a lady friend at a table in the back. Fireball pointed out Bill Pullman at a table on the sidewalk. Nic Cage walked in behind us, saw the other celebs and left in compliance with the Commoner/Celeb Ratio Law:

> *Hell-A Rule #7: No more than 5% of diners in a restaurant can be famous; the other 95% must be commoners. Of course, during Awards Month in February, when all the stars in the universe congregate in LA for the Oscars and the Golden Globes, the ratio rule is temporarily suspended.*

The lunch with Fireball, Michael, Pierce and Bill went well. Fireball took a copy of *Jane Blonde* home and called me that evening. Record time for a producer to read a script. He smelled money. I did, too.

And I was looking forward to the change. I had written 50,000 kilobytes of multidimensional characters, three-act plots and Kleenex moments. Several of my past specs had gotten within one "yes" of selling. A dozen smaller, lower budget, cool indie scripts had sold, a big studio had bought one of my pitches, and a TV cable pitch was purchased. But no big blockbuster spec sales. It was my turn, damn it.

Jane would be my key to Door No. 1, also known as the A-List.

As I said, *Jane Blonde* was high concept, franchisable and had the perfect role for a bankable actress. Since there were more bankable actresses every day with big action movies either being released or in production, everyone said *Jane* would sell.

Fireball wanted to attach himself as producer. I trusted Fireball. He hooked me up with David and Jason at Nevison. They collaborated on the script distribution list. It went out wide. We all uncorked champagne bottles that evening.

By the next afternoon several major production companies, including Gale Grazer's company, took *Jane* into the studios. They weren't interested.

Gale took the project to five studios before she gave up. Fireball got it out to other producers with their own financing.

Everybody loved the script. It didn't sell.

Oh, the agony and the ecstasy of working in Tinseltown.

The week I got the wrist-slashing news, David and Jason told me they couldn't figure out why *Jane* didn't sell. Everybody loved it. They promised to get it out to the right actresses, starting with Katie Portman, whose action comedy did $50 million that weekend.

So did Katie Portman really get the script? Had she actually read it? Or had slimy David not bothered to get *Jane Blonde* to Katie and lied to me about it? That's what I had to find out.

Chapter Four

WHOSE STORY IS IT?

Beverly Hills, Present.

Back at Nevison's conference room, David was fuming about being thrust into the unexpected role of lead hostage. He had far more important things to do. Far more important people to screw.

"The truth about *Jane Blonde* is, it didn't sell. Nobody liked it," David spat out. "Get over it."

"I saw the coverage."

Coverage is a report written by a bitter writer who's never sold a script and has to resort to writing "reviews" of other people's scripts to pay the rent on his roach-infested, 200-square-foot loft in the valley. Some analysts who do coverage make a sport of writing the cruelest reviews possible. They read their spiteful comments to other analysts over tequila and malicious gossip. They try to outdo each other's coverage with their backstabbing prose. That's one of the reasons coverage isn't shared with the screenwriter whose script is being covered. Another is that many times analysts don't actually read the script. They scan.

Scanning is good for the analyst since they can "read" and review a 120-

page script in less than an hour. Since they're paid only $35 to $50 per script they want to turn in as much coverage as possible before checks bounce and insufficient funds notices clogged their mail boxes. Scanning is bad for the screenwriter since any nuance or subtext will be lost, characters confused, and plots misunderstood.

The coverage on *Jane Blonde* was stellar by most Hollywood standards.

"Where did you get coverage?" David asked, squinting his eyes and taking a step backward.

"Your agency."

"How'd the hell you get that?"

David shot Jason an evil look. Jason edged toward the door. I saw the movement out of the corner of my eye and swung the MP-9 in his direction.

"Get back here."

"I have to go to the men's room."

"That's not happening," I said as authoritatively as I could. Then I turned to David and asked, "So did you give the script to Katie Portman?"

He looked away. "Yeah, she said it sucked. Besides, she's booked for the next two years."

"But you actually got it to her?"

David wasn't used to a client asking the question a second time. He looked truly indignant.

"Would I lie?" he asked.

Electronic notes from a Latin tango sounded from Jason's jacket pocket. He retrieved a postage stamp-sized phone and flipped it open to answer. As he was saying, "Hello," I lunged forward and grabbed it. I could hear a small female voice inside the phone, "Jason? Hello?" I hit the power button. The phone made some cartoon noises and turned itself off.

I held my hand out. David knew what I wanted: his cell phone.

"It's on my desk."

I didn't believe him.

"Do you have a spec going out this week?"

Specs are those scripts written by delirious writers in hopes of selling them on the open market. Sometimes 100 scripts sold in a good month. Prices started at $100,000 and blasted into the stratosphere from there. Recently a writer friend of mine and his partner got $5 million for their thriller script. Some writers and their agents got wealthy from the spec market. Some writers didn't. I fell somewhere in between.

CUT TO THE PAST:

Century City.

My first spec went out shortly after I had arrived in LA. Another writer referred me to his agent after reading a high-concept comedy I'd written. High concept meant it was commercial and could be a box office smash hit. His agent was one of the partners of a prestigious literary/talent agency. I'll call her Agent Orange.

Her office was in Century City, a mini-metropolis of tall glass buildings and short attention spans. The view driving in from Olympic onto Avenue of the Stars always made me feel like Dorothy approaching the Emerald City for the first time. All Technicolor green grass and freshly planted, flamboyant flowers with towering skyscrapers in the background. There was always the impression of driving onto a life-sized movie set, maybe because Century City had been built on land that used to be the back lot for Twentieth Century Fox.

When I walked into her office, Agent Orange stood up, thrust her hand out to me and cheerfully said, "You're overdressed."

I glanced down at my two-piece Versace rip-off cocktail dress and felt sick to my stomach.

The dress I so happily bought with a cash-advance check from credit card number 11, thinking it couldn't be more perfect for such a momentous occasion, became a giant sign that said: "Kick me. I'm new and I had a lobotomy yesterday." A lime-green prom gown and tiara would have been a better choice.

I so suck.

"I'm on the way to a party," I lied.

"You're overdressed for a party, unless it's the Oscars."

The Academy Awards were in March then. This was January. I sat down in a Herman Miller chair, trying to keep from slobbering.

Hell-A Rule #8: a.k.a. Screenwriter's Dress Code: Never over-dress. In fact, dress to unimpress. The proper wardrobe for a female screenwriter is well-worn designer jeans, a "cause" or retro T-shirt and tatty black leather jacket if it is "winter." The most important part of the look is double-take shoes. Boots are good. Anna Sui black leather knee boots with metal studs and flowers will get you invited back for another meeting.

"So I liked *Remote Control*," she said. "Good universal theme."

Everyone wondered what their life would be like if they'd made different decisions in the past. That's what my script was about: A man's magical remote control changes "channels" in his life rather than channels on his TV. With every click of the remote he launches into an alternative life based on decisions he'd made in the past. Of course, the hero decides "there's no place like home" and tries to get back to his old life again, but he has no idea what channel he started on.

It sounded like a sure sell to me. It did to Agent Orange, too.

"You're not repped, right?"

"Well, I met with an agent at Scribes of Confusion who's interested. Now I have to meet with the partners."

There was a moment of silence. Then Agent Orange tapped on her computer keyboard and said, "Today is Wednesday. If you let me take this spec out wide, I'll have it to these people on Friday for a weekend read." She turned the computer screen toward me.

The list read like a who's who of producers. It was like a dream. Just like I read in the scriptwriting magazines.

I was teetering on the edge of a million-dollar script deal. My mind was drunk with the prospect of being a real Hollywood writer. Living in a mansion in Malibu. Being invited to all the cool parties. Driving an Italian sports car. Wearing expensive designer jeans made to look old and worn by someone else.

"Okay."

Agent Orange stood up, shook my hand, and escorted me out.

"We'll take care of everything. I'll call you Monday."

Beverly Hills.

I was dizzy with the newness of it all. Man, that was easy. I get an agent, she sends my script out, I get a lot of money. I liked this career. I thought about stopping by Beverly Hills Exotic Cars on Wilshire on the way back to my apartment, but I really liked my old Saab and had an odd feeling of cheating on her if I looked at other cars.

I went home and called my mom. She was delighted to hear about my good fortune. It was a confirmation that I should soon be coming home to the safety of my family with an Academy Award and a fist full of dollars.

Monday morning I didn't dare go out of the house, so when my agent called I could respond to offers from studios during the bidding war I was sure would happen. My imagination soared with fantasies: one offer coming in at a measly half-mil. Then 10 minutes later, another studio bidding a million plus producer credit. And 5 minutes after that, my agent accepting $1.5 million for the script, rewrites, producer credit and a cute little red Mercedes two-seater thrown in to sweeten the deal.

I stayed in my office near the phone all morning. It didn't ring. Agent Orange must be fielding offers so fast she couldn't get a call in to me.

Yeah, right.

What I didn't know was this: I had a better chance of getting hit by a pulp-wood truck in Beverly Hills than selling a spec script in Hollywood, even at the height of the million-dollar spec market.

By 4:00 I'd bitten every nail to the quick including toenails. I'd given my dog three baths. I'd scrubbed the kitchen floor, baked Russian Easter bread and painted the stairway up to my landing. I couldn't stand one more nanosecond, so I called Agent Orange.

She took the call and said, "Universal bought a script called *Remote Control* last week with the same concept." *Remote Control?* Somebody ripped off my title! Somebody ripped off my story! Eventually, a movie starring Adam Sandler called *Click* would be made using a similar storyline.

My ears buzzed, as if I had been standing too close to a bomb going off. The bombshell blew up my house in Malibu, my exotic car, and my Hollywood A-List writer dream.

"Listen, I'm sending it out to a second tier of producers," she said listlessly, not even trying to sound convincing.

What? Huh? I'd been sideswiped by Universal Mind Think. Universal, like the *world*, not the studio. Writers are exposed to the same media and inspired by the same sparks of info-babble. There are a finite number of stories swirling around in the Story Bank in the Sky. Unfortunately, another writer beat me to market with that one. It was my first full body slam in Hollywood, but it wouldn't be my last.

My mom called to ask about how things were going and when I was moving home. I gave her a rundown of my meetings for the week and tried to wow her with stories about the famous people I'd seen in the last seven days. I didn't tell her *Remote Control* didn't sell, and she seemed to have forgotten about it.

She ended the conversation as she did every week by saying, "You never know, something may happen soon."

"You never know" became my anthem. You never know when your script will fall into the hands of the right producer who's looking for that very story. You never know when you're going to meet someone at Starbucks who will change your life. You never know when a limo's going to hit you in the crosswalk and end your pain and suffering.

Two weeks went by. *Remote Control* didn't sell. Folks said they love, love, loved my script, but they didn't buy, buy, buy my script.

So I was back to first base, square one, Beanie Weenies and rice.

I assumed since Agent Orange sent out my script, that she was my agent. Naïve, naïve. I hadn't heard the term "hip-pocketed" until I tried to send another script to her. Then I found out she wasn't really my agent, but had only represented that one script she thought would sell. I hadn't "signed" with her agency. I had been hip-pocketed and now found myself agentless once again.

No agent. No big spec sell. I was crushed, crestfallen and downright depressed for about 20 minutes. But then I did the only thing I knew to do. Start another script.

After all, tomorrow was another day they would try to beat me down. I had to be prepared.

BACK TO THE PRESENT:

Beverly Hills.

Ten years later agents still sent out specs, although it wasn't the Gold Rush of the 90s.

The air in the Nevison conference room was thick with disgruntlement.

David glared at me. "Of course I have a spec going out."

"Then give me your phone." Even an agent at a relatively prominent agency needed to catch return calls the first time. Phone tag was a waste of time. He definitely would have his cell phone on his person.

He handed over his cell. It had been set to the vibrate mode. I turned it off.

There was a knock at the door. Meek and cautious. A small voice on the other side said, "David, is everything all right in there?"

David looked as if he were ready to bolt. I took a preemptive step forward, jammed gun metal into David's $1,500 Zegna suit jacket.

"Everything's fine, Tiffany. Go away," David said.

A moment of silence from the other side of the door and then Tiffany said, "Well, okay, but I tried to call you."

"Go. Away."

"But you're due at Le Dome in 15 minutes. Lunch with Steven Scott."

Le Dome was 15 to 20 minutes away depending on traffic. If David left in 10 minutes, he would arrive perfectly late.

Hell-A Rule #9: Never arrive on time for lunch. It makes you look unimportant or worse, desperately unbusy.

David glared at me a moment. He took a breath and gritted his teeth.

"Call and cancel," he ordered Tiffany.

Through the door, Tiffany screeched, "But it took us two months to get this set up. Do you really want to cancel? You need to get him on the Matson & Abner project."

That was it. My agent was Le Doming an A-List director to convince him to sign onto Team Crap's project?

I kicked the chair away from the knob and jerked the door open. Tiffany must have been leaning against the door because she stumbled into the room, wobbling on her spiky heels toward the conference table. I saw another assistant in the cubicle opposite the conference room looking in at us.

I slammed the door, lodging the chair against the knob again, and turned to see Tiffany cleaning up the whipped cream from my mocha that had puddled on the table.

"I'll call and tell them you're on the way," she said to David.

All agents' assistants are agents in training. Miss Tiffany was no exception. One thing Tiff had that was an essential for any 10-percenter, as *Variety* calls them, is tenacity. She was determined to get David to Le Dome come hell or high drama. I wondered whether Tiffany would be the better choice for agent. At least she'd badger execs until they said yes.

"I'll say you're running a little late. Okay?" Tiffany polished the table with a clean napkin. Then she glanced over at David and said, "How late will you be?"

"He'll be very late. Like not showing up late," I answered and aimed the sleek black gun at Tiffany, who squinted at it a moment.

"That a prop?" She took a step away from the weapon.

"Nope."

"Huh?" Tiffany looked over at her boss for an explanation.

David slammed his hand on the table for emphasis and said, "I have a lunch meeting and I'm leaving now."

Tiffany spun on her heels and headed to the door when she saw the chair lodged against the knob. She stopped a moment, not quite sure what to do. David and Jason were almost to the door, when I ordered them to stop. They didn't.

I leapt to the door, showing them who was boss. I herded them back to the table with the barrel of the MP-9. All three avoided contact with the gun metal like it was coated with some lethal alien virus.

"Sit!" I commanded. Tiffany plopped in a chair instantly. Jason whimpered a little and sat down. David crossed his arms and stood defiantly at the head of the table. Two out of three wasn't bad.

"Whose story is it?" I asked.

David looked at me like he was wondering if I was having an episode of dementia. "Whose story is what?" he asked.

"This. What's happening in this room? Whose story is it?"

Blank stares from the hostage party.

CUT TO THE PAST:

Jacksonville, Florida.

Writing was my destiny. I found out by accident the summer night I almost killed myself again.

Suicide was something I amused myself with in my 20s. I was compelled to make a half-hearted attempt about once a year. I longed for the nothingness from which I had come.

One time I tried to smother myself in a beanbag chair after too many wine coolers. I passed out face down, but was rescued by a friend before brain damage was irreversible.

Another time, I drank a bottle of French burgundy and slashed my arms from my wrists to my elbows with a razor blade. There was a lot of blood, but the cuts were too shallow and all missed arteries. At least by then I had better taste in wine.

Other botched tries to off myself only led to apathy. I got bored with the concept of suicide, and my decade of living dangerously ended when I turned 30.

But that particular summer suicide night, a curious thing happened: I became one with the universe. No, I wasn't doing drugs. That was something I left to the less brave. I wanted to see the whole nasty world exactly as it was with no chemical filters — well, except the occasional guzzle of wine. I replaced pharmaceuticals with transcendental meditation and other natural mind-altering exercises that eased the pain.

So when it came to the part about becoming one with the universe, it was an epiphany, yes, but not totally unexpected. I had come to learn at an early age that you find God in the moment.

I demanded to know why I was here. If God couldn't give me a good reason, it was hasta la vista, cruel world. The answer came quickly. I was here because here I had hands, so I could write down who I was. It didn't make sense. I wasn't a writer. I wasn't interesting. Why should I write down who I was?

But right after that, a tidal wave of calm swept over me. I felt a sensation of no longer having the confines of a physical body. Then I expanded outward to the sofa, then the floor, then the room, then the apartment house, then the neighborhood. And at the same time, I was becoming the sky, then the planet, then the universe.

An acid trip without the acid.

I'm a good southern girl. No, make that a bad southern girl. So I realize that Baptists don't transcend. At least not like that. But *I* did. That's when a new floor of the high-rise of life opened to me. After that, I was able to see my path clearly. At every intersection a sign pointed in the new direction. I'd be blessed to always follow the path.

So if God said I was here to write down who I was, well, that's what I had to do. So I wrote little things on scraps of paper a lot. Just odd, annoying, prophetic kinds of things. Nothing to show anybody else.

But I had no serious interest in reading about writing or learning the craft of writing, or actually writing anything anybody would want to read.

Key West, Florida.

So I ignored the call to the writing life until I moved to Key West to become an artist, something I'd wanted to do since I was five.

Key West is a small island at the end of the Florida Keys and the Southernmost point of the United States. It's one and a half miles wide and three miles long. I wanted to live in the historical area and found the perfect place. It had been a cigar-maker's house and faced the cemetery. It was more rent than I wanted to pay, but Key West wasn't a cheap place to live.

Then came the impossible part. The gallery. A real artist was represented by a gallery. Key West was overrun with artists and craftsmen, playwrights and interior decorators, treasure hunters and alcoholics. So every gallery in town was full the day I arrived. But the next day a miraculous thing happened.

I tied a half-dozen samples of my work, baskets made from natural fibers, into a big bundle with a jute rope, strapped them to my back and made a dramatic entrance to Guild Hall Gallery. By the time I had walked from the car to the gallery I had an entourage of curious tourists interested in buying the baskets. So without planning it, I delivered a half-dozen buyers to the gallery along with my determination to become a member of the co-op.

I had been told the previous day that with a yearlong waiting list, there was no hope of a space at the gallery. Yet that very morning a ceramicist had suddenly decided to leave. With all the turistos trying to buy the work off my back, the artist who was current president of the co-op could see the potential. So I left my bundle of baskets for the other artists to see and went off to have dinner with my mom. She had come to Key West with me, hoping I would not find a gallery or a place to live easily, and I would forget about moving 12 hours away from home.

The next morning I went back and received an enthusiastic welcome as the newest member of Guild Hall Gallery.

So within three days of arriving in Key West, I had a Conch house to call home and a gallery to call my place of business. I was 500 miles from my mother's house in Northeast Florida and galaxies far, far away from my old life.

Once I got settled, I discovered that I was surrounded by writers. Tennessee Williams lived a couple blocks north of me.

Every afternoon around 5:00, Tom, Tennessee's real name, ambled down Duval Street past Guild Hall Gallery headed to cocktail hour. His bodyguard, Scott, was with him every day, and he'd wave up to me where I sat on the balcony weaving sculptures from local palm fibers. Tom always smiled and tipped his Panama hat with his cane as he passed.

I'd been thinking about writing ever since I'd moved to the island and one afternoon when I saw Tom and Scott coming, I dropped my work and took off down the stairs and across the street. I met them in front of Bubbles, a little café owned by friends.

I introduced myself and as we walked along, I said that I was a fan of his work and knew I was called to write I just didn't know how to get started.

He laughed and said, "Well, write, God damn it. Just write."

I searched for words to explain my trepidation. "I get the tenses all mixed up, and I'm not sure how to start or end a story."

Tom glanced over at me and laughed. Feeling like a fool, I wanted to evaporate into the ozone and forget about writing forever. But I just stood there and laughed, too.

"There's a class starting at the Fine Arts Center. Try that."

Maybe he wanted to get rid of me. Maybe he was being helpful. Either way, I thanked him and drove over to the Tennessee Williams Fine Arts Center the next morning and signed up for the creative writing course.

Tom asked how the writing was going when he'd see me on the balcony. I always said, "Great." I lied.

I was intimidated by syntax. I suffered through present tense/past tense schizophrenia. But I did what Tom had said. I wrote.

The last time I saw Tom was at a private reading of one of his works in progress. It was called "The Dunzinger Women." I knew Tom was an alcoholic. I knew critics savaged him. I also knew he was a creative genius.

I sat there with two dozen other people at the old Sands Resort and heard him read about two spinsters who took a young stud into their household. He stopped and sipped his bourbon. He stopped and wrote notes. It was magical.

A couple months later Tom was dead. He choked to death on a sinus spray bottle cap in the middle of the night. It happened in some lonely hotel in New York City. I remember seeing the headlines of the *Key West Citizen* on the way to Guild Hall. I stood there in front of the newspaper box reading the words, but not believing them. My heart went cold.

And it was Tennessee Williams, bless his troubled soul, and that damned writing class that led me to the hostage drama in the Nevison Agency conference room.

BACK TO THE PRESENT:

Beverly Hills.

I repeated the question: "Whose story is it?"

Jason finally worked up the courage to say something. "It's your story."

"Very good, Jason. And David's leaving, but not for his lunch meeting," I said.

"He's meeting Steven Scott. Who do you think you are, telling him he's not going?" As soon as she said it, Tiffany looked regretful. "I mean..."

"I'm the woman with the submachine gun. I think that puts me at the top of your A-List, right?"

Tiff studied the MP-9. "It's a prop, right, Dave?"

"How the hell do I know?" David darted for the door.

I fired off a few rounds into the ceiling to assure everyone that my weapon was definitely not a movie set prop. The recoil jarred my body, propelling me backward a step. My arms buzzed with energy from the blasts and the detonations left me deaf a moment.

Designer track lighting blew up. Plaster exploded. Hell hath no fury like a screenwriter scorned.

David threw his hands over his head and fell toward the wall. Jason, who was sitting at the table, slid off his chair, collapsing onto the floor.

Everything was littered by fine white dust from the plaster. The place looked like a Sunset Boulevard coke den on a Saturday night.

The smell of gunpowder wafted through the air and into my nostrils.

The incident sent Tiffany into elevated terror alert. She let out a little yelp, leapt up from the table and stumbled to the door, pulling at the chair lodged under the door knob. I charged her, shoving her backward into David.

He caught her, but quickly pushed her away. "Get off me."

Agents never socialized with their assistants, unless it was just a sex thing, and everyone knew that could be very dangerous. That meant that only the sexually addicted, self-destructive morons touched their assistants.

Tiffany started hyperventilating, careening around the room, literally bouncing off the walls like one of those 80s video game heroes. Then she stopped, her face buried in a corner. She started to cry.

"I hate Hollywood. My mother told me I'd die if I came out here," Tiffany sobbed. "Please, baby Jesus, save me and I'll go home like a good girl and marry Donnie."

David stood up straight, his shoulders back and glanced down at his Zegna threads. He brushed off the plaster dust. "I just bought this yesterday."

"For the Steven Scott lunch?" I hoped it was true.

David glared at me. Jason emerged from under the table and stationed himself back in his chair. He seemed, oddly, to be enjoying the moment. Maybe it was because he was a junior agent and never had the discretionary income to buy a Zegna key fob, much less a whole suit. Or maybe it was because nothing this exciting ever happened in real life at the Nevison Agency.

I peeked through the blinds to see panic on the other side of the glass. Gunfire was not an everyday occurrence on the second floor of the Nevison Agency. Agents and assistants were fleeing toward the exits. I could see the elevator doors open and people trampling each other to get in. Several agents were on their cells, calling the New York design firm of SWAT, no doubt.

I was running out of time. I was running out of coherent thought. I was running out of blood sugar. The sugar and caffeine from the mochas were catching up with me, propelling me toward a hypoglycemic fit.

My primeval fight-or-flight response took over. "Let's get out of here." Those five words ricocheted around the inside of my head.

I had to get out of there. I thought about bolting onto the street and catching the next taxi to Palookaville. But you can't hail a taxi on the streets of Beverly Hills. You must have a concierge call one. Besides, I didn't know where Palookaville was.

Then a calm overtook me again. It was like I had suddenly become one of my action heroines. I knew exactly what to do. I had to take hostages and flee the crime scene in the exodus of the others.

That way we could escape before SWAT could cordon off Canon Drive. They would try to establish contact with the hostage-taker, otherwise known as me. By the time they figured out the hostage-taker and hostages weren't there, we would be at the drive-in window of the "In and Out" Burger on Santa Monica getting a protein fix.

Brilliant.

Chapter Five

THE LATE ESCAPE

Beverly Hills, Present.

Tiffany made annoying little gasping sounds as she wept with her face in the corner. I was repulsed and sympathetic all in the same moment. Females had a disadvantage in the film business since a boy's-locker-room mentality ruled the studios, production companies and agencies.

> *Hell-A Rule #10: Never whine. Or if you must, do it in the privacy of your own boudoir in the darkness of night with the covers pulled over your head.*

Hollywood abhors weepy women.

I had a nightmarish childhood like a lot of females. I grew up poor, but I never used it as a reason for weakness. I couldn't afford a college education, but I made the best of things. When I was looking for my first job as a graphic designer, my potential boss asked if I had a boyfriend and if I could work late hours at his place. I walked out, started an advertising agency and put the bastard out of business. You'll never hear me whine. Well, almost never.

"Shut. Up," I said to Tiffany before I was aware of thinking it.

Tiffany half turned, her drugstore mascara oozing down her 20-year-old skin. She was the type of girl who probably auditioned for "American Idol" in the largest metro city closest to her midwestern hometown. But being neither an extraordinary singer, nor a tone-deaf egomaniac, she would have been of no interest to Idol's producers. In reality, Tiffany was a mediocre girl trying desperately to change her lot in life. Getting a job at Nevison wasn't easy, so I had to give her credit.

"Well, are you going to shoot us or not?" Tiffany squeaked. "The anticipation is killing me."

Tiffany had snapped, crackled, popped. Maybe she was one of those young women who pretended to be subservient, but who was really manipulating the hell out of everyone around her. She was such an expert at it no one knew, especially not the men. Maybe she wasn't from the Midwest. Perhaps she grew up in the South.

But she immediately regretted her outburst and said, "I mean, I don't want you to shoot us, but…"

"We're leaving. Everybody up," I commanded. That's when I noticed no one was sitting down except Jason, who stood up immediately.

"You're not taking us out of here, are you?" Jason asked. "I read this script last week where this cop said once a victim got in a car with a kidnapper, that their chances of surviving dropped to about 5 percent."

I hated when anyone started quoting criminal statistics. I wanted to drop everything and check my extensive crime library to see if they were right. Research was one of my favorite perks of being a writer and I enjoyed submerging myself in the world of the story with all its unfamiliar, prickly edges. So, I had every book known to crime writers on the shelves in my office back in Florida.

Come to think of it, maybe I was able to push myself into the kidnapping game with relative ease, because I had done so much research about hostage-taking for past screenplays.

"Okay, everybody out," I barked with all the confidence I could marshal.

Tiffany's eyes darted to David, who I thought looked suspiciously accepting of his predicament as he said, "Will this never end?"

I kicked the chair away from the door. It looked impressive, but the stunt caused a blast of pain at the end of my right big toe. There was no way I would let them see me cry.

"Out. Out. Out." I sounded forceful and in control. Yet in my head it was chaos. There was no clear plan. No outline or beat sheet to tell me what scene came next. It was real life. And it was damned exciting.

For a moment, I was glad I had met Tennessee Williams in Key West and he had suggested I take that creative writing course, which led to a beginning screenwriting workshop in Fort Lauderdale, which led to a master scriptwriting class at the International Film Workshop in Rockport, Maine, which led to a screenwriting conference in LA, which led to all the agents and producers I met at the conference saying I had to move to LA, which led to my moving from Florida to California two months later.

Over the years, I learned never to wait for someone else to make something happen in my career. I had to get out there and make it happen myself. Now, here I was greenlighting my own project. Yipee!

Kidnapping may be illegal, but a lot of things that happened in Hollywood were illegal.

Just as David stepped through the conference room door into the hallway, I realized that once my three hostages were no longer confined to a small room, there was a possibility that one or all would try to escape.

"Stop. Stop," I said. David came to a sudden halt. Jason banged into him.

Then Tiffany bumped into Jason. They turned to look at me.

I needed handcuffs. Why hadn't I thought of that? I'm sure my friend in Vegas had a lovely collection. Not necessarily for apprehending enemies, but primarily for kinky sex games with lonely neighbors, mostly female. I only knew about that because his ex-wife spilled her guts after their vicious divorce. No handcuffs? No problem. I would just improvise.

"Take off your belts."

Tiffany checked her waist, as if she wasn't totally sure which outfit she'd worn that day and said, "I don't have a belt."

"You two. Belts off." I motioned to David and Jason with the barrel of the MP-9.

They eyed me apprehensively as they slid off their belts. David's crocodile beauty looked like it was brand new. Jason's was well-worn, cheap, made-in-China imitation leather. He looked embarrassed or maybe it was just my imagination.

"Now buckle them together."

David glared at me. "No."

Oh, oh. A mutiny this early in the day would undoubtedly spoil my mission. I had to be forceful, commanding. Why hadn't I taken acting lessons? They're good for writers trying to understand character, motivation, and acting technique. It would be also handy at the moment to be able to project an authoritative voice.

"Yes," I said a bit too loud and a bit too screechy.

"I won't," David replied in a scary Machiavellian voice.

I hated to get physical, but there's a time for talk and then there's a time for other stuff. I pressed the barrel of the gun to his forehead. Of course, the safety was engaged, but he didn't know enough about weaponry to figure that out.

"You will," I insisted. I wasn't used to ordering people around, but I was beginning to like it.

David hesitated a moment, then reluctantly buckled his belt onto Jason's. When he'd finished, he jerked his head into a slight tilt as if to say, "What now, bitch?" I prayed this MacGyver contraption would work.

"Then run one end through one loop on each of your pants and buckle it."

There was a moment when I thought David was going to slug me. Any self-respecting man would have. Need I say more?

Jason took over the belt project and amazingly, the result worked like a giant circular leash, tethering the two agents together with enough leeway not to prevent movement, but to dash any hopes of individual escape. I didn't think Tiffany would have the balls to make a dash for freedom, so we were good to go.

Suddenly out of the room next door darted Cameron Diaz and a spectacularly dressed black man. They dashed between my captives and me. I guess she didn't suspect I was the suspect, the cause of the panic.

"Excuse us," Miss Diaz said as they brushed by and she and her friend disappeared around the corner.

I was so surprised to see her, it didn't occur to me until too late that a superstar like Ms. D. would have added a certain glamour to our hostage team. LA was lousy with celebrities. You never knew when you would come face to face with one.

CUT TO THE PAST:

Los Angeles.

You would think with such open access, a screenwriter could get their scripts to any star they ran into at Whole Foods. That's not how it worked. Some actors may be polite enough to smile and take the screenplay only to toss it in the recycling bin at home. But most would say send it to their agent, which was code for "drink hemlock and die."

If only I could have gotten scripts to all the celebs I ran into over the years: Nic Cage in a shop on the Third Street Promenade, Wesley Snipes in an elevator, Arnold…oh, forget Arnold, he's too busy with his non-acting/non-political projects now, Warren Beatty at the Polo Lounge, Steven Spielberg at Morgan Freeman's Christmas party, Morgan Freeman at his Christmas party, Oliver Stone when I was an extra in *Nixon*, Jodie Foster at a Women in Film event, Rob Reiner at a restaurant on Maple Drive, Mel Gibson at the Director's Guild, Dustin Hoffman and Dennis Franz at the after party for their film *American Buffalo*, Renee Russo bowling in sweats and no makeup, God bless her, and Stevie Wonder getting into his black Mercedes limo with license plate FNGRTPS at the Four Seasons. Enough name dropping already!

Whenever you were out for lunch with a producer or friend, you always sat facing the door so you were first to spot incoming stars. You never actually said anything to your lunch partner. There's a secret head nod, kind of a forehead tilt toward the door, used to alert anyone else at the table to a star's presence. Then nonchalantly, a napkin would be dropped or a waiter would be summoned, so lunch partners could check out the newly arrived star power.

Hell-A Rule #11: Never stare at a star when you're out in public. Although staring is mandatory if you're one of the squealing fans wasting your time watching stars arrive at the premiere of their newest flop.

At a party, everyone tried to maneuver themselves into the perfect position to spot important players before other anxious non-players saw them, all the while pretending to listen to their new friend reeling off imaginary projects they were working on.

Even if you were standing face to face with someone, chatting, they never looked at you. Their eyes darted around like a monkey having a stroke, searching for a star, an important new director, studio exec or agent.

It would have taken just one right contact to change my life for the better. But no. I was the idiot who obeyed the rules.

> *Hell-A Rule #12: Never beg for a celebrity to read your script and never carry a script with you anywhere, unless you are delivering it to someone who has asked for it. The best writers are never caught dead with a screenplay in their hands.*

And where did it get me? Here, standing at the exit ramp of destiny. Well, screw the rules, on with the show.

BACK TO THE PRESENT:

Beverly Hills.

"Head 'em up, move 'em out." I wasn't sure that they got the "Rawhide" cattle drive reference. Maybe they didn't watch TVLand on cable. But they proceeded through the door with Tiffany trailing behind. It was apropos, really. Hollywood execs operate with a herd mentality. If one starts charging toward a script or project, they all follow. Many of our best films were made by strays that refused to follow the herd. Most of our worst movies were made by the herd.

As we moved through the deserted cubicles, an assistant darted out and upon seeing us, retreated into the men's room. I knew every agency employee who had fled was already on his or her cell to LAPD, so there was no use wasting time rounding up one more trivial hostage. I saw the elevator doors close as we came around the corner.

I stopped our happy group a moment, searching for an escape route. There was a door beside the elevator labeled "STAIRS."

"Down the stairs." I poked the small of Jason's back with the muzzle of the MP-9, urging him to move. He pitched forward and stumbled into David. He shot an annoying look back at me. I guess being taken hostage kind of sucked.

Then I realized I had forgotten my backpack with its collection of designer weapons. I blamed it on sleep deprivation laced with caffeine overdose. I glanced back toward the conference room where I'd left the pack on the table. I knew I should march everyone back and pick it up, but the forward motion of the moment swept me toward the exit.

David hit the door to the stairs and we headed down the first flight of steps and into the bowels of the dank parking garage. David and Jason had a difficult time at first maneuvering down the steps because they were linked together by their belts, but they quickly got into the rhythm of it.

Miss Tiffany lurched down the steps in her 3-inch stilettos. She stumbled a couple of times, but caught herself on the steel railing. The last time, she broke one of her newly manicured fingernails.

"Damn. Damn. I just had these done at Juan Juan."   One   thing about people in Hollywood, in times of crisis their priorities are worn on their sleeves. To Tiffany, who had just spent two weeks' lunch money for one of the best manicurists in Beverly Hills, preserving her perfect fingernails was more important than preserving her life. She was beginning to get on my nerves.

We were halfway down the stairs when the door above creaked open and we heard footsteps dashing toward us. I peered up to see an attractive man with grey hair wearing a charcoal-colored suit. He stopped in his tracks when he saw me with the MP-9.

"Oh, God in heaven," he gasped. Then he turned tail and ran back up the stairs.

He must have been one of the senior partners. No one else would have been allowed to have grey hair.

Suddenly the fire alarm went off. Its piercing scream made me feel like I was being attacked by shrieking aliens from outer space. Everyone picked up the pace to flee the earsplitting racket.

We came out into the garage. There was an absence of sound except for the muffled ringing of the fire alarm from inside the building we'd just left and a commotion up the ramp outside on the street.

The usually bustling garage was serene. No idling cars, no starters sparking an engine to life, no valets squealing tires. I spotted the valet parking sign and through the window of the valet station I saw a young man reading a script. No wonder Nevison had such great coverage: the valets doubled as story analysts.

There are millions, maybe billions, of screenplays stacked on shelves, on desks, holding up coffee makers, being used as door stops, lining trunks of cars and clogging recycling facilities in the entertainment capital of the world. Scripts are copied, passed around, thrown away and some actually are made into movies. But not many. When someone reads a script they like, they should call the writer and say, "You know what? I really liked your script."

Do you think that happens? Rarely.

If the producer gets the coverage and it's somewhat positive, she reads the script. If she likes it, she passes it to Tom Hanks. Maybe he likes it. A lot. So Tom says he'll sign on if his aspiring writer friend can be hired to rewrite the script. In this case, the original writer would be the last to know about the script being made into a movie. It's just a formality to actually make an offer, sign contracts and pay the writer who came up with the concept. And no one ever calls the writer to say they liked the script.

"Hello?" I said to the valet as I escorted David, Jason and Tiffy to the valet station.

The valet looked up to see us standing there. He was a young good-looking thing with fashionable facial hair, nose stud and shaved head. He was either an aspiring filmmaker or rock star. If he worked for Nevison, he knew how important it was to dress the part. With his look, he would be out of the parking garage and in a studio by the end of the month.

Startled, he dropped the script he was reading on the floor. I looked down to see the title *Jane Blonde* and my name on the cover page. Well, this was encouraging. At least someone at Nevison was interested in *Jane*.

"What do you think of the script?"

The valet picked up the screenplay, tossing it on the counter. "Pretty good writing for a girl." So far he hadn't seen my weapon.

I thought about shooting him then, but decided to wait until after we got our ride. At least he was being honest. Women writers are at a terrible disadvantage in the American film business. On an average, women write only 7 percent of all Hollywood movies released in the U. S. That's a shocking number and it's been like that since I started writing screenplays. And women action writers are as rare as clean air over Burbank. It's not that members of the female species aren't slaving away at their Macs and writing thousands of scripts a year, it's that there's some wonky bias against them. It's a Young Boys Club in LA and everybody knows it. If anyone says different, ask them why 93 percent of all movies each year are written by boys.

"We need his car," I said motioning to David.

"Your ticket." The valet leaned out of the parking station door and held out his hand.

David checked his pockets. "My ticket's upstairs. It's the black BMW."

The valet scanned the cars. All black BMWs. Actually there were more new black BMWs in that parking garage than there were at the Beverly Hills BMW new car lot on Wilshire.

"I have to have your ticket. No ticket, no car." He said it with an *I may be a valet today, but tomorrow I'll be a star and then I'll make you pay* attitude.

"Get his car. Now." I stepped forward so the valet could see the weapon. For a moment, he studied the gun trying to decide if it was real.

I was weary of the skepticism. I was tired of my cannon being mistaken for a movie prop. I was kicking myself for not taking the missile launcher in my friend's munitions dump. He said no one would challenge me with that baby aimed at his cojones.

I braced myself and squeezed the trigger of the MP-9 and let off a jarring couple of blasts that left the valet station looking like a crime scene in "CSI."

Jesus, the noise was deafening inside the garage. My ears rang from the assault on my eardrums.

The valet howled and sprinted up the ramp to the street. He disappeared before I could even turn the weapon in his direction. Not that I would have actually shot him, although there was one valet I encountered in the past who deserved the death penalty for stealing my Robert Johnson CDs.

The racket left my hostages cowering near a FedEx truck, holding their hands over their ears.

"Get your keys. Come on, we're going for a drive," I said to David.

The three crept away from the FedEx truck. David glanced toward the exit.

"Hey. Just because I didn't shoot him…" I shook my head and looked as mean as possible. David took a step toward me.

"You know this is insane," snorted David. "LAPD probably has the building surrounded already."

"Then I guess we're all going to be famous on our way to the morgue."

Tiffany started to whimper again.

"What did I say about that whining?" The whimpering came to a sudden halt and she wiped her eyes. Jason patted her arm sympathetically. She edged in behind him, like he could protect her from the mad woman's fury.

"David, get your keys," I said.

David stepped into the valet station. The belt tether jerked Jason in with him. They got wedged between the door and the valet's stool while David nabbed his keys.

They shuffled back out. I took the keys from David.

"Where's your car?"

"How do I know? I didn't park it."

I guess he'd forgotten I lived in LA for eight years. I stepped into the valet station and scanned the keyboard. I was sure the place where David's keys had been hanging was marked 2-10. Garage level 2, space 10. As I turned to exit, I bumped into a stack of scripts on a counter in the corner of the tiny office.

There, second from the top, with black Magic Marker title on the spine of the script was BAJA TRIANGLE. I could hardly believe my eyes. I stopped, pushed the top script off and opened the cover.

Baja Triangle was one of the first pitches I sold when I moved to LA.

CUT TO THE PAST:

Beverly Hills.

A couple of months after moving to LA, a friend referred me to an indie film company looking for pitches, I was thrilled and skeptical. Why skeptical?

Hell-A Rule #13: You can't sell a pitch unless you've already sold one.

I hadn't sold one. But what did I have to lose?

I called the development department at the company and talked with one of the D-Girls. "D" as in development. They find scripts, read scripts and open their doors to one in one hundred writers. They develop scripts with the writers and then hand the screenplays off to the producers. That script may eventually become a film. Or maybe not.

The D-Girls gave me a list of parameters and countries where they wanted to shoot. A pitch meeting was set for seven days later. Cool.

Not really. When I got off the phone, I remembered I had never been in a real pitch meeting, one where the producers really needed to buy pitches and have scripts written. I panicked and ate an entire box of stale CocoPuffs.

After that, I called a friend who taught for the Writers Extension Program at UCLA and wrote action movies for the foreign market.

"No sweat," he said casually. "Just pull some old ideas out of your thriller file. Don't waste time on developing a story specifically for any country, just use a story that could be set anywhere and say it's set in the Philippines, or wherever."

He said no one was really going to pay me to write a script based on my original pitch, because no one had ever paid me before. Hollywood Catch-22.

It was good advice given in earnest from a screenwriting veteran. I chose to ignore it.

I launched into a no-sleep work schedule, researching every country on the low budgeteer's list, ending up with three thrillers set in Bali and Greece, and two action-adventures set in Mexico. I studied the cultures and religions of the selected countries, the topography, the political climate.

The day I went to pitch, I was having an out-of-body experience. I got those as advance warning when my life was about to change. I felt spacey and everything was hyperbolic. Colors were brighter, like I was inhaling pure oxygen. Objects looked more distinct, like I was watching life on 3-D TV.

I went, I pitched, I sold. They bought three of the five pitches. I called my UCLA friend to share the great news and he said, "Oh, sure. Don't write a word until you get the check and it clears."

I admired his unbridled cynicism. It was something I aspired to.

I got the first check and wrote the first 90-page script set in Bali in two weeks. It was a noir-ish thriller. They turned around notes in a week. I delivered a new draft the next week and was ready to start the second script, *Baja Triangle*, for them when I got a call.

Everyone at the company loved the Bali script. Everyone at the company wanted to go to Indonesia to shoot the film. Everyone at the company was being fired. The company was sold to one of the largest foreign distributors in the world. I could come pick up my final check at the front desk.

But what about getting my thriller made? That probably wasn't happening because the new company only wanted to acquire finished films.

What about *Baja Triangle* and the other pitch they had "bought"? Maybe someone else would be interested.

I crashed into a wall going a hundred miles an hour. One minute I was launching my screenwriting career, the next I was back to writing articles for *Nail Pro*.

A wise girlfriend who had been in LA for 15 years, surviving on party food and the kindness of strangers, advised me to find a wealthy boyfriend. Sponging off a man wasn't my style, although a boyfriend wouldn't be unwelcome.

I focused on work, writing *Baja Triangle* in little less than a month.

Soon I had optioned a couple of scripts, including *Baja*, to indie producers and had my name in *Variety* and *The Hollywood Reporter* when those deals were reported. I expected the studios to call. They didn't.

BACK TO THE PRESENT:

Beverly Hills.

The valet parking station at Nevison was not the place I would have preferred to discover someone ripped off one of my scripts, but that's where it happened.

On the title page under *Baja Triangle* were the troublesome words "Written by Chuck Green." I flipped to page one. It was my script all right, same opening, same character names. Chuck, whoever he was, didn't even have the decency to rewrite the first page or think of new character names.

I grabbed the script and flashed the title page to my captors.

"Who the hell is Chuck Green?"

David sneered at me. "How am I supposed to know?"

Jason shrugged.

Tiffy said, shyly, "I think he's one of those clients referred by that wacko attorney, the one with the red hair and bad teeth."

"Jimmy Tremont?" I asked.

Tiffany thought a moment, "Maybe."

"It was Jimmy Tremont?"

"Yeah, I think that's the name. I'm pretty sure," Tiffany replied.

Son of a bitch.

Jimmy Tremont was my attorney before Zen Man and the one who had stolen an option I asked him to secure for me. So did this mean, Jimmy created fictitious names to set up projects based on previous clients' scripts? I knew he was a bit mad, but the man was an attorney, for God's sake. He knew I registered all my scripts with the Writers Guild and they would produce a copy of the script if anyone plagiarized my work. Unless…the script was old enough for its registration to expire.

Here I was in the middle of a kidnapping and realized maybe I should expand my kidnappee list. That bastard, Jimmy Tremont. I'll bet he had a racket going with selling former clients' scripts after they fell out of WGA registration protection.

Adrenaline spurted through my bloodstream. My heart raced. I wanted to find Crazy Jimmy and smash his face. Instead, I shrieked and flung Chuck Green's script into the air, drilling it with a 9mm bullet.

David, Jason and Tiffany grabbed their ears and winced.

I added Jimmy Tremont to my Things To Kill List, if I survived the day.

I herded my charges down the ramp to the second floor, found space 10 and used the electronic lock on the keychain to beep the car open. I could hear police sirens in the distance.

"Inside. Now." Jason flopped into the backseat. With the belts tethered, the action almost yanked David to his knees beside the car.

"Jason, you little pig. Cool it," David said as he struggled into the backseat. I slammed the door.

I leapt into the driver's seat. Tiffany stood outside the passenger door a moment, as if considering her options. I jammed the key in the ignition and rolled the passenger window down.

"Tiffany?"

She stuck her head in the window and said, "Yeah."

"Aren't you coming with us?" I asked.

"Do I have to?"

I considered the question. Maybe it would be easier without her. Two hostages were plenty. I probably should let her go.

"Yes, you have to come," David ordered from the backseat. "If I have to go through this bullshit, you do, too."

Tiffany looked at me with pleading eyes.

"You can leave, if you want to," I said. If I were Tiffany, I would have turned and run like the devil was on my butt. Yet, she looked back at David a moment and then slid into the passenger seat, adjusting the back. David had a spell on her. Bastard.

About 30 seconds later we were squealing past the valet station with David and Jason slamming together in the backseat and Miss Tiffany bracing herself for more broken fingernails in the front. I locked the doors from the central lock. After all, I didn't want my prisoners escaping before the chase began.

I didn't know what to expect once we got onto the street. David could be right. Maybe LAPD had the building cordoned off already. Maybe the helicopters were there by now. SWAT could be waiting with their armored assault vehicles. The National Guard in their Hummers. The Beverly Hills cops in their limos.

Whatever was out there, we were going to confront it in about two seconds.

I revved the engine as we rounded the final corner headed to freedom or death. I hit the apex of the corner, drifted slightly in a perfectly controlled skid, slammed the Beamer into second, zoomed past the valet station, ran over Chuck Green's forged script and roared up the exit ramp.

The car went airborne for about five seconds as we sailed across the sidewalk and hit the street so hard the car bottomed out, making a sickening, metal-crunching sound.

"Don't screw with my car, damn it," David growled from the backseat.

Pedestrians fled. Cars on the street swerved to avoid us as I fought to turn the car without sideswiping parked vehicles. I almost had it until we slid by a new Rolls, peeling off the side trim.

David screamed, "Bitch, you're going to pay for this!"

In the rearview mirror I saw two cars crash into each other right in front of Nevison. Just as this happened, the first LAPD cruiser responding to the "shots fired" calls from Nevison smashed into the two wrecked cars, forming a perfect roadblock.

I couldn't have choreographed it better had it been on the page of a Final Draft document.

We sped north on Canon. Adrenaline pumping. Hopes of righting a wrong flooded my being.

Chapter Six

WHAT'S ONE MORE HOSTAGE?

Beverly Hills.

I was on adrenaline rush, fight-or-flight overdrive, and I knew I had to slow things down, especially the car. If I could flow with the traffic rather than the panic in my mind, there was a chance of slipping into anonymity in the river of drivers on Santa Monica Boulevard.

I stopped at the traffic signal where Canon intersected Santa Monica and started a yoga deep-breathing exercise, breathing in slowly through my nose and releasing through my mouth.

In front of us were the serene gardens of a Beverly Hills park that ran for several blocks along Santa Monica Boulevard. It was the place where the city held its annual arts festival, which attracted prominent artists and craftsmen from all over the U.S. When Christopher and I first met, we found ourselves wandering through the artists' booths, talking about art and how we would have a house together where we could hang paintings of the desert and original prints of the sea.

That art show demonstrated one of the few big disparities we had: how fast our brains processed information. I had a stunted attention span. Christopher was chronically patient.

Fortunately, we were able to work through the innate conflict caused by radically different interactions with the world and met in an embrace somewhere in the middle. He figured out how to put up with my knee-jerk reactions and I learned to cope with his maddeningly slow-motion stimuli responses.

As I waited impatiently for the light to change, I imagined the art show across the street in full swing among the roses, with Christopher and I strolling hand-in-hand through the paintings. It was a comforting respite, until I heard police sirens a short distance away.

I wondered if I should have turned at little Santa Monica, a block behind me.

One of the duties of traffic officials in LA is to make driving as confusing as possible. The fact that there are two streets named Santa Monica Boulevard running parallel to each other with one block in between is testament to how seriously traffic engineers take the "confusion factor."

It took three months of dodging traffic in West LA for me to realize that there were actually two Santa Monicas—well, actually three.

There was the two-lane Santa Monica Boulevard that the locals called "little" Santa Monica, also called "small" Santa Monica by my Russian girlfriend, Kira. Then there was "big" four-laned Santa Monica located just north of "little" Santa Monica.

The third Santa Monica was the eclectic beach town that was part of the LA metropolitan area and home to great restaurants, thousands of eccentric street people and an ocean so polluted that body contact was forbidden.

Driving in Beverly Hills had its challenges. There should be a guidebook to the secret regulations you had to deduce from repeated experiences. Here are a few:

Hell-A Rule #14: If four cars come to a four-way stop exactly at the same time, the most expensive car has the right-of-way. That is usually a Rolls, although some custom limos or vintage cars can take precedence.

Hell-A Rule #15: If you drive an American car when you move to Beverly Hills, you are required to donate it to charity within 30 days. Only hip foreign cars can be licensed in the 90210 zip code. An exception is certain classic automobiles made in the U.S.A., but they must have original upholstery and paint.

Hell-A Rule #16: Rolls and Mercedes must only be black, white, gray, silver or very dark colors. Anyone driving a bright red Rolls hasn't had money long enough to know better. Gold Rolls and Mercedes are only driven by sheiks from the Middle East or crown princes from some obscure country in Europe.

The light turned green. There was an immediate horn blast from the car behind me. I raised the MP-9's muzzle so that the rude-assed driver could get a glimpse. The irritating noise stopped.

That's something you learned in the South. When you're being followed down a dirt road in the middle of the night by suspicious assholes in a pickup truck, you just raise your firearm so it is clearly visible through the back window of your Camaro. Either they back off or you get a shotgun blast to the trunk. Either way, you have to take the risk.

I eased the BMW onto big Santa Monica. It was a beautiful day, so I rolled down the windows. Life was good. I was cruising toward the beach in a shiny Hollywoodmobile with leather interior. It was the kind of car that came with "feeling-of-wellbeing" as standard equipment. Too bad I had just become one of LA's Most Wanted, otherwise a stroll down the Third Street Promenade and lunch at The Ivy at the beach would have been just the thing.

Fortunately, as we drove further away from the crime scene, the police sirens became more distant. I couldn't remember if this was a part of my Coffee Bean Napkin Plan, but it seemed right for the moment.

Traffic slowed as we approached Wilshire. I was in the right lane and feeling righteous. I turned on the Smooth Jazz station and found John Tesh.

Yeah, yeah, I know, he's so not cool. But I liked his music. Besides, he seemed like a nice guy when I saw him and Connie Sellecca at Century City Mall with their new baby when I first moved to town. He was one of my first celebrity sightings.

One of the things I had to get used to when I first moved to LA was the impulse to rush up to every familiar face at the mall, thinking they were a someone I knew from back home. They always turned out to be a character actor I'd seen on TV or in films so many times that my brain perceived their facial features to be those of an acquaintance or long-lost family member. I learned to ignore the familiar faces and hoped I didn't snub a friend from Florida who was in town to work on a movie.

We inched forward in traffic as cars turned right at Wilshire. Just as I felt warning signs of a hypoglycemic attack, I heard the sound of an electric window being lowered. Out of the corner of my vision field, I saw movement in the backseat. Jason had his leg and head out the window in an escape attempt. A very brave, brainless attempt by a fairly spineless individual.

"Where do you think you're going?" I swung the MP-9 around so he could have a clear view of the hole where the bullets exited. David gave him a scorching look and Jason withdrew his extremities from the escape hatch.

I checked and the belts binding them together were still intact, although it occurred to me at that moment that they could easily free themselves.

I shot an evil look in David's direction and said, "Let him try that again and you'll have 150 pounds of dead meat at the end of your handcuffs."

Good dialog wasted. I'd never remember it when I was writing that action-adventure I had planned for jail. If I didn't get the words on paper right away, they evaporated into the ether.

"There are no handcuffs," David said in an irritated voice.

"What?"

"You said handcuffs. We're not handcuffed."

Well he knew what I meant. Jesus.

"Is that your only note?"

No response from David.

Everyone in Hollywood had notes or comments on your work. Even if they hadn't read your script or treatment, they had notes. Usually things that made no sense. That's how decent scripts turn out to be indecent movies. Stupid notes should be illegal. Banned. Buried in salt mines with yesterday's nuclear waste.

In the line of traffic, we waited through two lights to turn onto Wilshire Boulevard. That was a much more scenic chase route just in case the police and news choppers found us and initiated a televised pursuit.

I hoped there weren't many other police chases happening at the moment, because I needed breaking news coverage. It would be a shame if all the news crews were occupied with other pursuits and couldn't broadcast ours live. A wave of anxiety came over me as I wondered why the police hadn't located us yet. The sooner we had a police escort, the sooner the news director at KCAL could assign a chopper.

Another hunger pang hit me. The caffeine from the mochas was doing its job of lowering my blood sugar. My thinking was getting fuzzy. I needed protein. Fast.

We finally got to the intersection and I made the turn onto Wilshire Boulevard. I hit the accelerator. For some reason this stretch of Wilshire was rarely in total gridlock, so I swerved through three lanes of traffic in a frenzy to find cooked cow.

After suffering from hypoglycemia since I was 25, I knew that the best thing to fix me in a blood-sugar emergency was a fat hamburger. It was the amino acids. Either that or hamburgers had a powerful placebo effect. I knew from experience that blood-sugar deprivation can make one do illogical things.

CUT TO THE PAST:

Beverly Hills.

Shortly after Christopher and I had met, we were out shopping for Mother's Day gifts. Years earlier, Christopher had stopped giving his mum an offering to acknowledge his gratitude for her carrying him in her womb for nine months, changing his poopy nappies, and shaping him into the compulsive obsessive he was. His lack of Mum's Day presents had something to do with the feminist he'd lived with in New Zealand for 10 years. She didn't believe in spending money on others during "commercial" holidays.

I insisted he make restitution for all those lost Mother's Days, so we were driving to the Beverly Center when my blood sugar crashed. So did my car.

It happened so fast. One moment a debilitating hunger swept over my body and I growled, "I've got to eat." The next minute, the front of my car was rammed up the butt of a Mercedes Benz convertible. Well, actually, we just collided at five miles an hour, which is top speed on any street leading to the Beverly Center. My brain was so disoriented from glucose starvation that all I could think of was protein. I had to have protein. Now.

The driver's door of the Benz opened and Hannibal Lecter stepped out. It was really Sir Anthony Hopkins, but he had that Chianti-slurping look in his eyes.

I slammed the gearbox into reverse and smacked into a Ferrari behind me. Ray Liotta leapt out.

My next action wasn't triggered by two rabid movie villains descending upon me, it was sheer biological panic. I hit first gear and fled the scene in search of a burger and fries.

Christopher was so shocked, he was mute until I swerved into a strip mall parking lot where I saw a Vietnamese deli advertising an Oriental burger.

"What the hell are you doing!?" Christopher finally asked as I jumped out of the car, headed into the deli for a protein fix.

"I have to *feed* the beast!" I shouted back at him.

I had ordered and was already devouring a bag of potato chips from a display rack beside the register by the time Christopher joined me.

"Do you know you're wanted for hit and run?"

"Want some chips?"

He just stood there watching me consume more fat calories in one minute than I usually had in one day. I tore into another bag as a police officer strolled into the deli for a chat.

It all worked out since I collapsed just as the officer was reaching for his stun gun and I was taken to Cedars-Sinai's emergency room across the street. I don't remember much about it until I woke up with glucose pumping into my veins.

Christopher was there. As my thinking processes began functioning in a somewhat rational way, I found out about the chaos I had caused on the street. Instead of being distressed, I was grateful I hadn't accidentally committed vehicular homicide in my hypoglycemic stupor.

The damage to the Mercedes and Ferrari was minimal. My insurance company paid the claims and then raised my premium. It was a dramatic way for Christopher to learn about my lifelong struggle with low blood sugar, but I figured if he didn't leave me after my momentary madness, he'd sign on for the long haul. He did. He also started carrying a protein bar with him in case of crisis.

BACK TO THE PRESENT:

Santa Monica.

How I wished I had one of those protein bars with me as I sped west on Wilshire, past the opulent high-rise condos lining the boulevard. We crossed into Santa Monica. Nearer the beach, there was an abundance of vegetarian cafes, vintage clothing shops and rollerbladers. The community was home to thousands of homeless people and transients. They were treated with dignity and given services like food and shelter instead of rides out of town as Beverly Hills did.

There was a farmer's market on Second Street during the week and several art house film theatres. There were also about half a dozen municipal parking garages where I could ditch David's BMW if I needed to.

In my descending hypoglycemic fog, I couldn't remember exactly where "In and Out" Burger was. Maybe another burger joint would do.

There are very few fast food places with drive-in windows in this part of town. I was especially sure I couldn't manage taking three hostages and a semi-automatic weapon into Islands without being noticed.

McDonald's on Wilshire near Fairfax flashed across my cortex, but that was east of Beverly Hills and miles away from where we were now. Also it was not an option, since that area was too near the Nevison Agency and would be cop city by now. So I took a quick left and got back down to big Santa Monica, hoping to find a fat, juicy "In and Out" burger there somewhere.

When I saw the sign two blocks away, I sped up, gleeful to know I would be saved shortly.

I drove up to the drive-through.

"Anybody hungry?" I said to my passengers.

I angled the rearview mirror to be able to keep a watch on David and Jason.

"You're actually going to eat that crap?" David asked. I knew he was only trying to make me feel bad and he probably secretly chowed down on the delectable burgers on his dateless Saturday nights.

Jason shook his head and said, "No thanks."

I looked over at Tiffany. "I'd love to have an order of fries, but I can't." She smoothed her sweater over her protruding hip bones.

I got two orders of fries for Tiffany and two burgers, super-sized fries, and a milk shake for me. I pulled into a parking space in the back of the restaurant and opened the bags.

"You can't eat that in my car," David said.

"I think we can," I replied and handed fries to Tiffany. I convinced her to eat the uber-calorie fare by reminding her this could be her last meal.

I scarfed down my food and Tiffany shared her fries with Jason, while David was forced to witness our fast food binge. His fancy car began to smell like deep fried spuds and charred beef flesh.

My blood sugar surged. I was a new woman. I adjusted the rearview mirror, drove up to a dumpster and tossed the trash, slammed the car into reverse, sped out of our "In and Out" sanctuary and headed to the beach.

"What's Katie Portman's address?" I asked anyone who was listening.

There was no response from the back seat. In the rearview mirror I could see David giving Jason the "another crazy writer" look.

"She's somewhere above Sunset, right?" I'd read it in *Entertainment Weekly* or heard it on one of those star-sucker TV tabloid shows.

"How would I know where Katie Portman lives?" David was giving attitude again.

I slammed on brakes in the middle of big Santa Monica. Cars swerved by. Horns honked. This time the horns were my friends. They stressed out David. His head snapped around to see a black Hummer bearing down on us.

"You're going to get us killed," he yelled.

"You think?"

The Hummer sped by, narrowly avoiding us.

"What's her address?" I asked again.

"I have no idea. I'm not in talent," David replied.

"Well, that's quite obvious. Call her agent. Get her address."

There was no chance I was believing a senior agent at Nevison didn't have Katie Portman's home address, home phone, cell and fax numbers. Or at least if he didn't have them stored in his Blackberry, he could get them from someone else at the agency.

"You shut the whole place down. Remember? And you took my cell phone. Remember?" David's voice sounded angrier with each word.

"We have everyone's cell number, though." Jason was trying to be helpful.

He asked me, "You have a phone, right?"

David eyed Jason warningly.

"I'm just trying to end this with as few fatalities and dismemberments as possible," Jason said quietly to David.

"Stop trying to be funny, Jason. You're not that clever," David said.

Defiantly, Jason leaned forward and began reciting someone's cell number, "Three one oh…"

"Zero, not oh," I said, correcting him. "It's a number, not a letter. I hate when people use the English language willy-nilly."

"Three one zero, five five five, one three one three. That's Carrie in talent. She'll have it."

One of the remarkable things about junior agents and assistants to agents, most of them had master's degrees from Harvard or Yale. Many had photographic memories.

I glanced in the rearview mirror to see David staring out the window, his jaw tight with rage.

Miss Tiffany overcame her paralysis and addressed me, "Do you realize you're parking in the middle of Santa Monica Boulevard? You'll get a ticket."

It was one of the smartest things I'd heard her say.

"You're right."

Here I was, a fugitive from the law, and I was drawing attention to myself by impeding the flow of traffic on one of LA's busiest streets. I drove on. We were almost to the Pacific Ocean. A decision had to be made.

I tossed my cell phone to Tiffany.

"Call somebody. Get the address."

"Nobody will give it to her. It's confidential," David muttered from the backseat.

"Say it's a life-or-death matter," I said to Tiffany.

"Nobody cares," said David.

"I'll fire off a round."

"Nobody cares." David said those two words slowly, like I was mentally challenged and couldn't understand.

Tiffany handed back my cell phone and said quietly, "She lives in Bel Air. Oracle Canyon Road, 238."

"Damn it, Tiffany. You're fired." David looked like he meant it.

"Good, because I'm tired of sucking your weenie."

I glanced over at her. She looked like she meant it.

"That's sexual harassment." I looked like I meant it.

David leaned forward and spat out, "She doesn't mean it literally."

Jason started laughing. David smacked him. He kept laughing. David smacked him again.

"No fighting." I raised the MP-9 as a warning.

"I'm sorry." Jason had the giggle bug and it was causing trouble.

David slugged Jason and immediately grabbed his hand in pain. "Jesus. That. Hurt."

Obviously David had never had to resort to hand-to-hand combat. He seemed surprised that smashing his fist into another human being's skeletal mass would be painful.

I was determined to get to Katie Portman's house. The more I ruminated about it, the more I was certain she hadn't gotten the script, hadn't read the script and would love the story once she got the script.

Jane Blonde was perfect for her. It was funny, had a lot of girl-kicks-ass action and left the door open for franchising. Sequels are an important part of the Hollywood profit equation. Any smart writer knew that. Any smart actress knew it, too. Fireball, my indie producer, said it was a big part of the appeal of *Jane*. So going back to the question that occupied every square inch of my brain for weeks: Why hadn't the script sold on the spec market?

> *Hell-A Rule #17: If you're a screenwriter, never write a high-budget spec script with a female lead. A chimpanzee would be a better bet. Studio execs will only greenlight a big budget movie if it has certain male actors who guarantee a tsunami of ticket buyers on opening weekend.*

Maybe Katie Portman wasn't interested in doing another action movie. Maybe she wouldn't like the script or the character. Whatever she thought, I wanted to hear it directly from her. I needed to know the truth.

When Santa Monica Boulevard ended at Ocean, I took a right and eased down to the Pacific Coast Highway, one of the most spectacular drives of Southern California. It's where the natural ocean meets the unnatural civilization of materialism gone mad. For miles, two- and four-lane blacktop crowns leveled cliffs providing a view to the horizon.

Driving to Sunset, only 15 minutes to an hour up the coast, depending on traffic, was enough time to remind me of my many trips with Christopher up PCH to Santa Barbara to escape the skull-crushing pressure of LA.

What would Christopher think of all this? It was an impulse, yes. But an impulse that had been growing like a cancer inside me for a daze of days. He would sympathize. He wouldn't be surprised. He wouldn't dump me and go back to his cold-hearted feminist in New Zealand. Or would he?

For the first time I thought about how life would be if we were apart. We'd only been together for four years, but I couldn't imagine being without him. One day, when all of the planets aligned and fate gave its blessing, we would be married.

Christopher was Heater Man, keeping me warm on winter nights. He was the one who laughed at my margarita-induced jokes. He was the love of my life and light of my darkness. I realized I was getting into Jonas Brothers' territory and brought my sappy daydreams to a halt.

I grabbed my cell phone, turned it on and hit Christopher's speed dial number at work. He answered on the first ring.

"Hey, honey," I said nonchalantly.

"Liz, where are you? Are you still in LA?" His Kiwi accent sounded strained.

"Ah, yeah. Sorry I didn't call before. I've been kind of busy."

From the backseat, David shouted, "Busy kidnapping her agents."

"What was that?" Christopher asked.

"Hold on," I replied. I laid the cell phone down and raised the gun for David to see. He shut his mouth. I put the pistol on the floorboard and picked up the cell.

I said to Christopher, "Oh, that was David making a stupid joke about agents."

"Is everything all right? You didn't say anything about going out for meetings," he said. I could hear people in his office talking in the background. I think I heard one of them say something about me.

"It was important. I had to come out today," I said, hoping he wouldn't ask why.

"Why? Why did you go without telling me? What was so urgent?"

It was comforting to hear his voice, yet I was beginning to regret I'd called him on an impulse.

"This isn't about *Jane Blonde*, is it?" he asked.

"*Jane Blonde*? Well, yeah, actually," I replied.

"Did you get a deal? Is that what this is about?" Christopher was being optimistic. That was good.

"A deal? Well, that's a possibility." I couldn't lie to Christopher. There was this trust bond between us and I wasn't willing to break it under any circumstance.

"What do you mean, a possibility? What's going on, Liz? Tell me the truth."

Oh, God, kill me now. The person I loved the most on the planet asked me to tell him the truth about what was going on: That I had lost my mind and kidnapped my agents and a perfectly good assistant and was headed to a siege in the Bel Air mansion of Katie Portman.

I pulled off PCH into a restaurant parking lot so I could focus on the consequences of the situation.

I could have ended the call then, but that also could've led to the end of the relationship. I wasn't going to risk that. I could have pretended static on the line was compromising the transmission, but that was too overdone and lame for any screenwriter with any self-respect to do.

"Liz, honey? What is going on?" pleaded Christopher.

I was compelled to spill my guts.

"I've kidnapped David and Jason and Tiffany, and we're going to Katie Portman's house."

Anyone who knew me less would have laughed and said, "Oh, yeah, right. Very funny."

But Christopher said, "Let me make sure I heard you right. You kidnapped your agents and you're at Katie Portman's house?"

"No, we're on the way to Katie Portman's house."

"But you said you kidnapped your agents, right?" he asked, carefully analyzing the situation.

"Yes and their assistant," I replied.

There was a moment of dead air and then Christopher blasted, "Have you gone completely mad? You've got to let them go, turn yourself in and throw yourself on the mercy of the courts. What the hell were you thinking?"

I couldn't think of what I had been thinking.

"Liz, are you there?"

"I can't," I said finally.

"You have to. They'll send you to prison, do you realize that?"

"I've already done it. They're in my car now. I mean, David's car."

David leaned forward and barked, "*Call 911, damn it!*"

"911? Who said that?" Christopher asked me.

"David. He wants you to call 911," I said grudgingly.

"You carjacked your agent's car with your agents in it and David wants me to call 911?" Christopher asked.

"They'll send me to jail anyway, so just let this thing play out," I begged.

"Where are you?" he asked.

"On PCH. Chris, remember when we used to drive up to Santa Barbara?"

"Stop it. Don't you change the subject. You have to stop this madness right now. Right now. I can't marry a woman who runs off in the middle of the night to commit some capital offense 3,000 miles away!"

Marriage. There was that word again.

"But Chris, you know what happens when we try to get married."

"It won't happen again," he promised. "Come home right now, and we'll go down to the courthouse tomorrow morning and get married."

My mind was dizzy with the thought of it. Christopher and I, finally man and mad woman after all these years.

He continued, "Otherwise, I'm gone. If you don't end this right now, I'm leaving."

"You wouldn't."

"I will," he said convincingly, so convincingly that I believed him.

My heart broke. I couldn't live without Christopher. But I couldn't live with myself if I gave up now.

"Chris, I love you more than an Academy Award, but I can't quit now."

I didn't wait for his reply. I pressed the power button, turning the cell phone off.

Everyone in the car was quiet.

"So are you going to let us the hell out of here?" David said, spitting out the words like they were spoiled sushi at Matsuhisa.

"Not on your life," I said defiantly and drove out of the parking lot onto PCH.

"Where is Oracle Canyon?"

"Ask Concierge GPS," Tiffany said helpfully.

"What's that?"

Tiff pointed one of her remaining perfectly manicured nails to a little button above the rearview mirror where a tiny red light was flashing. I got a sinking feeling in my stomach when I realized what the blinking light was: a global satellite tracking system. I'd stolen a car that anyone could see on a location tracking screen. Oh, perfect.

"Kind of like OnStar or LoJack, but with advisories about the hottest new scene. Concierge can tell you the exact directions from here. Just call them."

Her finger was almost on the button before I grabbed her wrist out of the air.

"Owie!" she shrieked. "I was just trying to help."

"GPS? You mean they can track us?" I asked, my mind reeling with the idea of being tailed by some piece-of-space-junk spycam miles overhead.

I glanced in the rearview mirror to see David almost grinning.

LAPD could track us wherever we went. Maybe that's why we hadn't seen the choppers. They were hanging back, keeping up with our whereabouts by GPS.

I refused to be outsmarted by a stupid agent and his technocratic car. I hit the gas.

Pacific Palisades.

The Pacific Coast Highway was the westernmost road in the quiet cliffside town where Steven Spielberg and other film-biz illuminati lived. Restaurants dotted the west side of the road, sandwiched in between oceanfront homes and vast expanses of Pacific seascape.

This was one of those moments when I was happy that I knew the neighborhood, remembering that the massive parking lot beside Gladstone's Seafood was coming up fast on my left. I downshifted, caught a break in traffic and swerved into the entrance. Even at lunch they had cars lined up for valet parking.

You would think that the coast of Southern California would be lousy with seafood restaurants, but Gladstone's was one of the few in LA. Maybe it was because the ocean was so polluted there were no fish and half of the year was off-limits to swimmers. There were no shells on the beach, no signs of aquatic life whatsoever. I called our edge of the Pacific the Dead Sea.

The scarcity of cafes serving cuisine from the sea made Gladstone's wildly popular, even though none of the seafood on the menu was local. Christopher and I took Mum and his sister, Barbara, there when they visited just before the aborted wedding. They both ordered the green-lipped mussels from New Zealand.

Gladstone's was a big place, with an extended deck overlooking the waves. In nice weather, one of the wooden booths built like picnic tables was the best place to eat crab and lobster. There was freedom to splatter sea creature juice all over the table and yourself. Inside dining was casual, as well, with a giant barrel of peanuts in the waiting area where patrons could munch on peanuts and throw the hulls on the floor.

I hated to drive into Gladstone's parking lot without stopping to eat, but the pull of my hero's journey ruled.

I stopped our getaway car behind three cars near the valet station, grabbed the pistol from the floorboard and tucked in my jacket pocket.

I turned to look at David and Jason and said, "One word, one look, and you'll all be victims of a spectacular mass murder."

More dialog evaporating into the ether.

"Are we having lunch? I love the mahi here." Tiffany looked hopeful.

A valet trotted up to the car. I flipped the central switch, unlocking all the doors.

"Everybody out." I was enjoying being a bossy-boots, as Christopher called me on occasion.

They talk funny in New Zealand.

I got out and handed the keys to the valet, who was a well-groomed, shiny-faced kid who looked about 16. "Welcome to Gladstone's. Have a nice lunch," he said cheerfully as he grabbed David's keys.

Tiffany got out and was coming around the side of the car toward me when

I realized that David was trying to get out one side of the car and Jason out the other. Since they were still leashed together, they were going nowhere fast.

The valet had already jumped into the driver's seat and pretended not to notice the turmoil in the backseat. I stepped around the car door and peered in at David and Jason struggling against each other.

"Out this way," I said, indicating Jason had to follow David out of the car. Jason turned around and looked at me almost pleading for me to let him win this small battle.

I said to Jason, "Look, this will all be over soon and there's going to be a lot of press coverage. I'll say nice things publicly about you and every agency in town will want to hire you as a senior agent."

A moment and then Jason followed David out of the car. I slammed their door closed.

Tiffany headed toward Gladstone's as the valet sped away

"This way." I said it loud enough for Miss Tiff to hear. She stopped and looked over at me.

"No mahi?"

"Get over here."

For an instant it looked as if she was going to make a break for it. She glanced at the deck of Gladstone's where dozens of diners were scoffing down mahi mahi and beer.

"Now!"

Tiffany did her pouty thing. She moped back to our happy little group. I hoped the valet hadn't noticed David's and Jason's tether. Even if he had, I was certain he'd seen stranger things in this parking lot.

I escorted my charges south away from Gladstone's. Visitors strolled the sidewalk between the parking lot and the beach all the time. We didn't look suspicious. Well, except Jason and David kept bumping into each other as they walked. David glared at Jason like he was responsible for this whole misfortune.

Glancing back at the valet station, I saw an older SUV pull up, a couple get out and head into Gladstone's. One of the six valets drove it to within 20 feet of where we were near the end of the parking lot, far away from the valet station. As soon as the little guy jumped out, I was there with the artillery.

The valet was Latino and had an in-your-face "I'm such a macho man" aura about him, making him seem much taller than his 5'2" height. He wore the mandatory Gladstone's valet uniform: black pants, white shirt and red vest. But instead of the usual black tie, he wore a stunning turquoise and silver bola.

He seemed more amused than shocked at my display of armed force.

"This is 'Punk'd,' right? Where's the camera?" He said in a Mexican accent. He glanced around for the hidden camera.

"No camera. Just a gun."

He studied me a moment with his deep brown eyes and laughed again. "Yeah, right. That's funny."

I jabbed him with the MP-9. He pushed the gun away.

"Hey, I'll sue you and your network. Don't mess with Fifi."

"Fifi?" David's disinterest shattered a moment.

"Fidel Bartolo Javiero Rafael Estevez," Fifi said nobly, holding his chin in the air and his head at an aristocratic tilt.

"Any relation to Emilio Estevez?" David was always going for the celebrity connection just like everyone else in this stinking place.

"Maybe," Fifi looked down his nose at David.

The social discourse was over.

"Everybody in," I ordered, indicating the old SUV.

Tiffy immediately jumped in the front seat and sat obediently, a bit like a clicker-trained lab. Maybe she was getting the hang of the hostage role. Maybe she enjoyed the thrill of it all. Maybe she was determined to get out of this in one piece so she could go home and marry Donnie.

Jason started climbing in the back, but David held his ground.

"I'm not going anywhere. You'll have to shoot me to get me in that thing."

Then David lunged at me, but since he was tethered to Jason, David's body sort of snapped back against Jason. They both fell on the parking lot pavement.

I stood over David, giving him an ECU (extreme close up) of the MP-9.

"In the car!" I instructed.

He and Jason scrambled into the backseat of the SUV.

That left Fifi and me. He backed away, looking as if he were ready to sprint any minute. "Nobody screws with Fifi," he said.

"You want to be famous?"

The fear and machismo vanished, leaving his ego naked and in plain view.

"What do you mean?"

I motioned him closer and said in a whisper, "I mean, do you want to be on TV?"

"I used to be a soap star in Mexico. I was very hot." He smiled charmingly.

It was believable. He emitted a seething sexuality that would be perfect for soaps. He'd had work done on his teeth and he was young enough to make a go at Hollywood.

"I can see that. So you're in LA looking for a break, right?"

He took a gulp of air and said breathlessly, "Are you a producer?"

"No, but they work for Nevison." I pointed at the rancid duo in the backseat.

Fifi peered in the SUV at David and Jason and then looked back at me.

"No shit? I've been sending headshots to Nevison for a year. They won't take my call."

"They will now." I smiled. Fifi smiled and then leaned in the open door and asked, "You are agents at Nevison?"

David ignored him. Jason smiled proudly, "Yes, we are."

Fifi leapt into the backseat with David and Jason. One second he was a tiger, the next he's a pussycat. It's amazing how the pursuit of fame changes a person.

I hopped into the driver's seat and made sure there was no On-Star, LoJack or Concierge GPS. We all buckled up and I adjusted the mirrors.

I cranked her up, slammed the SUV into gear, and roared out of the parking lot. Fifi waved to his fellow valets as we drove by. They just stood there dumbfounded.

"So, you in talent or lit?" Fifi asked Jason.

"Lit," said Jason, leaning forward talking over David, who was in the middle.

"But you know people in talent?"

I stopped at the traffic light, waiting to cross PCH to Sunset. The traffic was stalled across the intersection a moment and I felt that old stress knot coiling up in my tummy.

"Definitely." Jason said, eyeing Fifi. "You have a great look."

"Crap! Give me a break," David blurted out.

Fifi ignored David, focusing on Jason's compliment. "Thank you," Fifi said, with almost a blush. I wasn't sure if he really was humble or was pretending to be.

"You know, he may be perfect for John Sayles' new film," Jason gushed to David. "They're looking for a fresh new Latino face."

"Can you just shoot me now?" David asked me. He was having none of Jason and Fifi's future plans.

Fifi smiled over at Jason. "You can hook me up?"

"Sure. No problem."

I glanced in the rearview mirror. If I wasn't mistaken, there was some serious flirting going on between Fifi and Jason. David looked like his head would explode any moment.

Chapter Seven

ON A MISSION

Pacific Palisades, Present.

The cruise from PCH up Sunset was always beautiful. This day was no exception. One of the reasons millions of people crammed themselves into a few square miles called LA County was because you could drive with their windows rolled down year round, unless, of course, you had asthma or emphysema. Then you had to have your car hermetically sealed, use a HEPA filter, and bring your own oxygen.

Sunset Boulevard is wide and winding, the perfect autocross course if everyone stayed home. Dozens of varieties of palms, bird-of-paradise plants and other tropicals line the road, creating a lush corridor dotted with mansion after mansion behind high stucco walls.

Santana was playing on the radio. If my life had a soundtrack, it would include vintage Santana, no doubt.

I wasn't sure what we'd do when we got to Katie Portman's house. I ran a series of scenarios through my mind:

1) We'd get to the gate and I'd just talk with her through the intercom to ask if David had actually sent the script to her. I knew there would be a gate

and intercom because no star of Ms. Portman's fame and great fortune could afford to chance a visit from a random stalker or home invader.

2) If her people wouldn't let me talk with her on the intercom, I could scale the wall and attempt a face-to-face chat, although I wasn't sure what I would do with my lovely collection of hostages. At that point maybe I could just let them go. On the other hand, maybe not.

3) Or, perhaps, I could talk my way inside and bring my entourage. Anything was possible. Well, maybe not.

"Watch out!" Tiffany screamed.

I surfaced from mission planning just in time to spot two black cats dashing across the six-lane road. I floored the brake pedal. The SUV didn't have antilock brakes and it fishtailed into the lane next to us. Fortunately, there was no other vehicle occupying that space and I was able to straighten the thing out before we rolled, crashed and burned.

"That was two black cats," whined Tiffany clamping her hands over her head. "Oh, my, God. Black cats."

Jason leaned forward from the backseat and said, "It's just a stupid superstition, Tiffany. Nothing ever happens."

The cats scampered across a supernaturally green lawn toward a wrought-iron fence, slipped between the bars of the fence and disappeared into a tall hedge bordering the yard.

"What about that time we broke the mirror bringing it up on the elevator? And that afternoon our computer network crashed, we lost our biggest client and someone stole my iPod."

"Coincidence," said Jason as he sat back. I saw him and Fifi exchange admiring glances.

I drove on. Tiffany removed her hands from her head and twisted in her seat to look back at Jason.

"No, Jason. Everything happens for a reason," Tiffany said. "Just because we can't see something or prove something, that doesn't mean it doesn't exist."

Fifi chimed in, "Like my dead grandmother. She used to visit me every Saturday night about midnight, no matter where I was. She always said the same thing: cerdo. Which was strange because she hated pork."

"Maybe she was talking about you," David said maliciously.

There was dead air for a moment and then Fifi challenged David, "What do you mean?"

David replied, "Pork. Pig. Same thing."

Fifi unbuckled his seatbelt and leaned over Jason to confront David.

"Are you saying my grandmother calls me…pig?"

I looked back, grabbed Fifi by the shirt sleeve and pushed him away from David. "Hey, hey, put that seatbelt back on. You never know when we'll have…"

I turned back toward the road just in time to see the truck in front of us stopped dead in the street. I slammed on brakes as hard as I could, but it was too late. We skidded. My foot dug into the brake pedal and my knuckles went white from a panicked grip on the steering wheel.

Our stolen SUV crashed into the shiny yellow Ford truck in front of us. Thank God our SUV was too old to have airbags or that would have been the end of the road for us. We rocked to a stop, knocking the breath out of everyone except Fifi, who was not wearing his seatbelt.

Poor Fifi bashed into the back of the front seats and fell onto Jason and David's feet.

"Get off me, you undocumented asshole." David pushed Fifi away.

A frightening growl came from Fifi's throat and he launched up off the backseat floor board and grabbed David by the throat.

David shoved him away again. Jason hooked an arm around Fifi's shoulder and wrestled him back into the seat beside him.

Fifi was speaking in Spanish or maybe it was tongues, unleashing an angry storm of words in David's direction.

I saw the driver of the Ford truck get out to inspect the damage. He looked like an old football player with a neck as thick as his head and thighs the size of my waist. He wore the biggest eyeglasses I'd seen since my childhood. My Uncle Bill used to have, and probably still has, the same frames.

Truck Guy obviously wasn't from my old neighborhood in Beverly Hills.

Hell-A Rule #18: Never wear last year's eyewear. Any designer eyewear sold and worn within the city limits of Beverly Hills has an expiration date. After six months, a self-destruct mechanism triggers, transforming the out-of-style frames into a pile of melted plastic. It's best that the glasses not be on your face when this occurs.

Truck Guy took his glasses off and leaned over to have a look at his fender.

Thanks to the black cats, I wasn't going but about 15 miles per hour when our front end connected with his rear end. My first reaction was to climb out of the SUV to apologize and exchange phone numbers with Truck Guy for insurance purposes. I felt terrible that my usual civil behavior would be over-ridden by lawless panic.

"Put that seatbelt on. You're going to need it," I shouted to Fifi.

I checked behind us. Two lanes of cars were stalled about fifty feet back. I popped the SUV into reverse and gunned the accelerator, backing around in an arc. Then I stomped on the brakes, put her in drive and took off around the yellow truck.

Truck Guy screamed unintelligibly and threw something at us. I think it was his trailer hitch that had fallen off after I uncoupled our vehicles. It hit the back of the SUV with a metallic thud. Great arm. Maybe he was an NFL quarterback.

Fifi buckled his seatbelt and said to David, "Don't you ever insult my grandmother again."

I saw David in the rearview mirror glaring at Fifi. I didn't need anymore fighting between them. I was stressed out enough. So I said, "I saw a ghost once."

Nobody cared.

And I didn't care that they didn't care. I told them about Christopher and I going up to Bishop to my partner Bill Kelley's spread, the Rocking K Ranch, and how a working weekend turned into a session of ghost storytelling.

CUT TO THE PAST:

Bishop, California, Eastern Sierras.

William Kelley and I met in Rockport, Maine, when I'd started writing scripts. I was his student at the International Film Workshop where he was teaching a master class in screenwriting.

Bill was a legend in the biz. He wrote television episodes of classics like "Gunsmoke," "Bonanza," and the coolest of all, "Route 66."

While my fellow students were writing away at night as we were supposed to do, I was hanging with Bill and his saintly wife, Nina. By the time I was enjoying our last lobster dinner sitting across the table from Bill, I knew I was destined to suffer the hellish life of a true Hollywood screenwriter.

A few years later, when I lived in LA, I looked Bill up to discuss optioning one of his novels, *The Tyree Legend*, so I could adapt it into a script. He liked my writing and suggested we work on the script together. He'd won an Academy Award for co-writing *Witness* and I was a greenhorn, so I accepted his offer with glee.

Christopher and I went up to the Rocking K Ranch in Bishop, California where Bill lived so we could work on the film story together.

Bill and Nina's house was built of rough-hewn wood and stone. It was surrounded by a stream that flowed down from an Eastern Sierras mountain, split in two at the north end of their property and gurgled peacefully down to the neighbor's yard. The guest room was on the end of the house with windows overlooking the deck, desert, and the mountain beyond. It was paradise.

The first night Christopher and I were there, I woke up in the middle of the night and saw a man standing at the end of the bed. The deck lights were still on outside and I clearly saw the dark figure of a man blocking the illumination through the window.

I sat upright and shook Christopher awake. Just as I did this, the man turned and seemed to disappear out the door. As he fled, I could see he wore a cape or some sort of fringed jacket with strips of cloth or feathers.

My heart was racing as Christopher gained consciousness. He groaned and mumbled, "What?"

"There was a man in the room," I replied, trying not to sound panicked.

Christopher pulled himself up onto his elbows trying to wake up. "A man? Was it Bill?"

"Definitely not."

"It was just a dream, honey," he coaxed as he reached for me, trying to pull me into his arms.

I got out of bed and saw that the door was still closed. That's when I realized that the figure had not gone out the door, but through the wall closer to the bed. Yes, definitely through the wall.

Knowing I wouldn't rest until I had unraveled the mystery, Christopher turned on the lamp and joined me at the spot where the aberration made his getaway.

"He…well…he went into the wall. Here," I explained.

"Did you say *into the wall?*" asked Christopher.

It may have been our first discussion about the supernatural. I realized that I must sound like a crackpot to Christopher. But at 2 a.m. the supernatural always seemed even more supernatural.

Christopher opened the door and we searched for the caped intruder. There were no lights on upstairs in Bill and Nina's bedroom. No sign of a burglar or mass murderer. Nothing. I didn't sleep the rest of the night, afraid I would miss another paranormal event.

The next morning when I mentioned our visitor to Bill over breakfast, he casually said, "Oh, that was Wovoka. One of the Paiute warriors. A ghost dancer. The house is built on one of their war grounds."

Bill took a gulp of his vodka and orange juice and asked, "So what did he say?"

Until that moment, I wasn't consciously aware that the ghost dancer had spoken to me, but all the words came rushing out of some dark crevice of my memory.

"Wonka ah-tawa or something like that," I answered, amazed at my recall ability especially since it was a foreign, or in this case, native language foreign to me.

"Probably Paiute for 'Get the hell off my land.' " Bill laughed and headed out to the deck for another orange juice and fire water. We sat there until lunch telling about personal encounters with the supernatural.

BACK TO THE PRESENT:

Pacific Palisades.

As I told the story to my captive audience, every time I said Christopher's name I felt like a teenager talking about her first true love. By the end of the tale, I longed for Christopher to wrap his arms around me that very moment and tell me this was just a dream. Somehow, some way, this mad dash at solving the *Jane Blonde* dilemma had to turn out right.

The ghost story worked with my captors. Fifi seemed to forget about David's insult. After I finished, he said, "In my country we have everyday magic."

Tiffany joined in, "What's everyday magic?"

"Well, like my grandmother. It was no surprise to me the first time she visited. There is a little line between the livings and the deads in my town. Things happen we do not explain."

Just like Hollywood.

Tiffany turned around and actually looked at Fifi. She said, "That's what I was saying."

We were blasting along Sunset as fast as we could blast in heavy traffic. I half expected to see the yellow truck in the rearview mirror, but there was no Truck Guy or cops.

"Magic is bullshit," David said quietly.

I glanced in the rearview mirror to see Jason cutting his eyes at David. Fifi was ready to come out of his seat again.

"Don't provoke him, David," Jason said. "Everybody has their own stuff."

"And his stuff is seriously screwed up," said David.

That was it. Fifi unbuckled his seatbelt and pounced on David again. Jason was in the middle trying to keep them apart.

"Stop. Stop. Stop," Jason pleaded, swatting at both men.

Fifi and David called each other nasty names and flailed about.

"You fight like an old Chihuahua," Fifi screeched.

Just what I needed, a backseat full of gay bar brawl. If I hadn't been under such stress, it would have been hysterical to watch Fifi and David savaging each other.

Tiffany was an island of cool in a sea of bedlam as she noted, "You need to turn left at the next light if you still want to go to Katie Portman's."

I swerved into the turn lane behind two exotic cars waiting to turn left. The one directly in front was an Aston Martin. Its license plate said STARBOY. I wondered who was driving. Maybe the kid who plays Harry Potter or it could be some wannabe. In LA, you never knew.

The signal light turned yellow. The first car in our turn lane shot through the intersection and turned into the canyon road, but Star Boy just sat there until the light turned red. Bastard.

I rapped my fingers on the steering wheel, checking the rearview mirror repeatedly for bad news.

Fifi and David had exhausted themselves. They were taking a breather when Fifi said, "You hurt my big finger. Look, you drew…blood." He spat the word blood out like he was in an Off-Broadway soap opera, dramatically and overwrought.

I turned around to see Fifi jabbing his forefinger at David. If there was blood, I couldn't see it. David turned away, making a face like he smelled something bad.

"Let me see," Jason said, inspecting Fifi's finger. "It's just a little scratch."

David sneered and said, "He's a pussy."

Jason held Fifi back and hissed at David, "Would you just lay off?"

"Oh, afraid your new boyfriend will get hurt?" David said tauntingly to Jason.

There it was out in the open.

Some people in Hollywood preferred to keep their sexual predilections to themselves. Some people flaunted it. Jason was in the first group of closet freaks who pretended to go to Vegas for the show girls and gambling, when he really went to see the World Salsa Championships and the Forever Satin and Sequins drag show.

Jason smacked David and snapped, "Shut. Up."

David wouldn't quit. "Maybe you should tell him about your little problem," he said to Jason, emphasizing "little."

"Shut up, David." Jason punched him in the arm.

David was the bully who kicked wet sand in your face when you were down. The bully who stood over you and laughed when you fell off your new bike at your birthday party. The bully who ran your car off PCH and into the Pacific Ocean.

Leaning over and smiling at Fifi, David said, "He can't get off unless " It's a Small World" is playing, and there are two midgets in the room watching."

Hell-A Rule #19: Never, ever talk about your sex life, especially if it's twisted, even to a friend or co-worker you deem trustworthy.

Hell-A Rule #20: There are no trustworthy people in Hollywood.

Tiffany laughed a huge hee-haw snort.

Jason sat stunned, not blinking, looking as if he'd stopped breathing.

Fifi comforted Jason and said, "I love Disneyland. My sister went to see It's a Small World twice when we were there last year."

Jason was quiet a minute, frozen in the horrible moment of revelation, and then said, "Well, at least I'm not skimming cash off clients' accounts."

"He's stealing money?" Fifi asked and then made a shame-on-you gesture with his fingers.

"He's embezzling, committing fraud, and suicide," Jason answered.

"And he's bonking the boss's wife," Tiffany contributed.

Jason burst into laughter and said, "You're so fired."

All eyes were on David, who curled his upper lip into a snarl and snapped, "Screw everybody."

Tiffany continued, "Just because Nevison's a Scientologist doesn't mean he won't go nuclear on your ass when he finds out."

CUT TO THE PAST:

Beverly Hills.

Bill Kelley had called me to ask what I thought about lecturing for the Hollywood Writers Society, The Church of Scientology's creative writing group. He knew I lectured often at screenwriting workshops and thought he'd heard me mention the society.

Bill knew the woman who was the president and she had invited him to speak at their monthly meeting. I told him I had lectured for them three times and their writers were eager to learn. They'd be appreciative of his time and wisdom. Bill agreed to speak and we scheduled a dinner together for when he planned to be in LA.

Two days before he was to arrive, I got a phone call from him.

"Why the hell didn't you tell me they were Scientologists!?" he roared. I had never heard Bill's voice raised in rage and was unprepared for the assault.

"I asked you about them and you didn't tell me. What kind of friend are you?"

"Bill, are you talking about the Hollywood Writers Society?" I asked, my mind reeling from his outrage. "I thought you knew their president and had spoken to her group before."

"I spoke to another group she was with, not this group. I will not associate with L. Ron Hubbard devotees. They're lunatics!" he ranted.

"Well, I really didn't realize. I thought you knew who they were. They're harmless, really."

"Harmless?! Harmless as Satan's minions. Have they got you brainwashed? Are you one of them?" he asked, conspiracy theories surfacing in his field of vision.

"No, of course not." I laughed, which cast rocket fuel on the bonfire.

"You think this is funny?" he growled. "Those weirdo pissants put my name on their website and now it's all over the Internet. Bill Kelley, once a God-fearing man, is in league with the damn Scientologists. It's your fault. You lied to me!"

He slammed down the phone. I staggered, as if physically struck by his fury. I sat down on the sofa and stared out at the roses on the deck. Aggie hopped up beside me, sensing something was askew in our world. As I stroked her head, I tried to reason out the best way to repair the damage. Maybe I should call the Writers Society contact.

Hell had just been visited upon the president when I called. She was handling it better than I — after all, she was a Scientologist. She regretted the misunderstanding, was sorry Bill would not be speaking to her group, but would not allow Bill's irrational wrath to spoil her beautiful day. She said she would write him a letter and invited me to speak in his place. I did.

During my time in LA, I spoke to the Hollywood Writers Society numerous times. It was like presenting a workshop for any group. There was nothing unusual about them, except big stars were members of their mother organization, the Church of Scientology. Before each speech, the Writers Society invited me to be their guest for a gourmet dinner at Renaissance, the Scientologists' restaurant located in their "Celebrity Center" on Franklin in Hollywood.

The center is housed in a restored grand hotel surrounded by lush gardens, a greenhouse and good vibes. Renaissance's dining room is on the ground floor of the building and is wrapped on three sides by atriums with glass walls and ceilings. It wasn't unusual to see famous faces dining among the hanging plants and gurgling fountains. On my first visit, the society president introduced me to John Travolta, who was dining alone and graciously welcomed visitors.

I became friends with one of the group's members, a man who followed up after my first lecture with e-mail questions about writing. Although Jack had been a Scientologist for years, he never tried to recruit me or even talk about the benefits of conversion. He invited me to the Scientologists' annual gala at the Celebrity Center.

The grounds were converted into one spectacular bash with music provided by Scientologists Isaac Hayes, Chick Corea, and Edgar Winter. The main parking lot was closed off, carpeted and lined with sushi bars, roast beef stations, seafood buffets, vegetarian banquets, dessert extravaganzas, and champagne fountains. Everyone was always glancing up at the tower, where the real VIPs mingled at the private President's Club party. There were whispers of sightings: Tom Cruise and Nicole Kidman, John Travolta and Kelly Preston, Kirstie Alley before she blew up, and her hunk *du jour*.

Near the end of the evening, all the guests gathered for a tribute to their founder, L. Ron Hubbard, or LRH as his followers call him. A giant portrait of LRH in his prime was projected onto a screen behind the stage, while current leaders reminded the true believers of their roots.

Upon departure, guests were given a special publication of LRH's writings with pictures from his worldwide quests: adventurer/explorer, daring deeds, unknown realms, letters, journals, and literary correspondence.

After the Scientology riff with Bill Kelley, he didn't call me for two months. I was depressed since our work on *The Tyree Legend* had come to a crashing halt and our friendship was fractured.

One afternoon the phone rang and it was Bill. He apologized for his outburst and said he realized I wasn't to blame for his lack of knowledge about the Hollywood Writers Society.

I quickly accepted his apology and he told me he'd been in New Orleans to research a new script. Bill had to "walk the land," as he called it. He wanted to include a mystical character in his story and had gone to a fortuneteller in the French Quarter for a reading. His idea was to take notes so he could create an authentic subplot based on the woman. But instead of inspiration for his script, he got inspiration for his life.

The gypsy told him many profound things, including that he had hurt an important ally and friend and that he must right the wrong. Bill was certain I was the ally she was talking about and heeded her warning by calling me as soon as he returned home.

We resumed our friendship as if the chasm of those two long months never existed. He never raised his voice in anger toward me again. We focused on more positive things: writing and selling *The Tyree Legend*.

BACK TO THE PRESENT:

Bel Air.

The light had turned green, but since few intersections in LA have left-turn signal lights I was still waiting behind Star Boy. There was a momentary break in traffic and Star Boy made the turn. I was determined to make it across as soon as the light changed to yellow.

There was silence in the car as David sulked about the disclosure of his criminal pursuits by his closest enemies. Fifi and Jason whispered to each other.

The green light changed to yellow and then red as I waited in the middle of the road for the last idiot running the light. Finally everyone stopped and I accelerated into Oracle Canyon. As I did, I saw a flash of yellow in my rearview mirror.

It was Truck Guy. He made the turn with me. I braced for a bump, but none came. Instead, angry Truck Guy sped past us, veered in front of our SUV and slammed on brakes.

I'd like to say that I was prepared for his suicidal maneuver and that I swerved around him and took off down the road, losing him in the process. But unfortunately a sad case of repetitive action overtook me and once again we smashed into the crumpled rear of his lovely truck. The SUV's engine stalled out.

This time Truck Guy was on me before I could flee or roll up the window. He grabbed me by the ear and pulled.

I yowled as he yanked my head half out the window. My seatbelt wouldn't let me go any further. I prayed my ear would stay attached to my head. I struggled to free myself, fumbling with anything that felt like a seatbelt release button. I think it was Tiffany who popped it loose.

Truck Guy yelled, "*Get the hell out. I'm calling the cops.*"

He let go of my ear and was trying to get my door open. I was determined to keep it closed.

"Look, I'm really sorry, but you can't call the police. I have hostages here," I said rubbing my ear and checking for blood. None.

"I don't care what…" Then it sank in. "Hostages?"

"Right," I confirmed as I tried to lock my door. "I'll give you my information, but there's this thing I have to do and…"

"Hostage? Like kidnapping?"

Befuddled Truck Guy pushed his last-century glasses up on his nose and looked inside the SUV to inspect my human cargo. Then he squinted his eyes, studying me a moment.

"That's bullshit. Get out of the car." He yanked at the door.

"She's wacko, buddy," said David. "Insane. Lights on, nobody home."

Tiffany looked out of my window at Truck Guy and said, "And she has a gun and she likes to shoot it."

"Bullshit," said Truck Guy.

I raised the gun into his line of sight.

It was like the car had just become electrified. He jerked back away from the door, holding his hands out as he stepped away. He put his butt in reverse and back- pedaled to his truck.

He jumped into his wreck and took off up the canyon road.

By this time there was a line of traffic behind us. The driver immediately to our rear had witnessed the drama unfolding and zoomed around us, not wanting any part of the confrontation.

The others blew their horns. It was annoying. Here I was doing my best to avoid attention and anyone within earshot was looking our way.

I knew Truck Guy would be on his cell phone calling 911, so we had to flee the near crime scene.

I tried to start the engine. It turned over but didn't catch. I tried again. Cars started passing us when oncoming traffic allowed.

I was still trembling from the spurt of adrenaline caused by the altercation with Truck Guy. When I thought about it a moment, I realized how close I came to having my ass kicked in the middle of this Bel Air street.

Hell-A Rule #21: Never have your ass kicked in public unless there are paparazzi there to document the event and the ass kicker is either famous or wealthy or both. Then you can sue their privileged butts for enough to get out of show business and retire to a beach house in Florida.

Physical confrontation was never a minus in career development of Hollywood players. It usually added to their legend, their mystique. Of course, I didn't have a legend or mystique to add to, but I never backed down.

I'm not saying I liked starting fights, yet I have somehow found myself in the middle of scuffles in the past.

CUT TO THE PAST:

Santa Fe, New Mexico.

Bill Kelley and I had been invited to teach at the Screenwriting Conference at Santa Fe. Bill and I had met 10 years before when he was the teacher and I was the student. Now we met in Santa Fe as peers, both teaching master classes to eager students.

We taught our respective classes the first day and enjoyed a long dinner for four with our significant others that night. The second day went well until Bill verbally attacked one of the conference directors on stage in front of the entire group of a hundred-plus attendees.

It started out as a minor thing, really. Bill made a joke about a point of disagreement on writing technique recommended by the conference co-director, a droopy little man I called Sad Sack.

Sad Sack defended himself in a surprisingly vicious way. Bill came back at him laughing and said, "What do you know? You've never had a movie made or won an Oscar."

Everyone laughed except Sad Sack. Apparently Sad Sack and Bill had a few unpleasant words after the panel. That set up the most notorious event of that year's conference.

The faculty was invited to a special dinner at an open-air cantina. All you could eat and drink. It was a fiesta with music, margaritas, and mucho musings about show biz.

After a few rounds I noticed Bill at the head of our table glaring at someone in the distance. I followed his line of sight to Sad Sack.

An admirer asked Bill a question about his Academy Award and he launched into his Oscar stories, forgetting about Sad Sack for the moment. I went back to conversation with Christopher and a producer friend.

Suddenly I heard a shout from the center of the cantina patio. I looked over and saw Bill faced off with Sad Sack. Although Sad Sack was 30 years younger than Bill, I knew that if Bill threw a punch, Sad Sack would be down and out, if not worse. Bill had been notorious for his knockout punches when he was a champion boxer in the Air Force.

Without thinking, I leapt from my chair and had Bill by the arm inside of five seconds. Sad Sack's partner was there by then, pulling Sad Sack away from Bill. I'll never forget the look on Bill's face, so much rage and hate. Sad Sack was spitting out vile nouns like has-been and drunk. Bill countered with adjectives like jealous and no-talent.

Bill lunged or stumbled toward Sad Sack. Sad Sack tried to get free of his partner, flailing his fists in Bill's direction. By this time, half of the faculty members were on their feet, some gathering around. It reminded me of high school, except no one was chanting, "Fight. Fight."

Bill balled up his fist and shook it at Sad Sack, "You little pissant."

I grabbed Bill's arm with both hands and said, "Bill, don't hit him. He's not in your class in boxing or writing." For some reason he found that amusing and laughed, breaking the spell.

I hauled him back to our bewildered group, depositing him at the head of the table again. He quickly began a story about being a champion boxer when he was young and said I was one of the best seconds he'd had.

Not knowing what a second was, I just nodded and smiled. Later I found the definition in the dictionary: *to support a fighting person in combat or to bring up reinforcements*. I was proud to be Bill's second, both in a cantina brawl and in screenwriting.

Shortly afterward, Bill wrote a marvelous book about a white soldier traveling the segregated South with his black boxing teammates. *The Sweet Summer* got published and there was talk of a cable movie being made.

We kept Bill away from Sad Sack for the rest of the conference. Needless to say, Bill wasn't invited back the next year. Neither was Sad Sack. The conference partnership broke up and Sad Sack's partner hijacked the seminar.

BACK TO THE PRESENT:

Bel Air.

The SUV's engine groaned as I switched on the ignition, but it wouldn't start. Again and again I tried until I thought the battery was going dead. Finally the engine roared to life.

I checked the rearview mirror. No cops. Just irritated motorists in a hurry with no patience for derelict American cars.

We took off up the road headed for Katie Portman's and Dream City.

Chapter Eight

GETTING TO THE A-LIST

Bel Air, Present.

We cruised up Oracle Canyon, ascending into the clouds of affluence and eccentricity.

Bel Air is one of the places in metropolitan LA where the mega-millionaires live. Almost 9 percent of the residents share the same skin color, greenish white. They are Caucasian primarily, but the color of money tints their lives, their philosophies and their perspectives.

The community is perched above Sunset overlooking the less fortunate in the flatlands of West Los Angeles. I wouldn't want to own one of these pompous palaces, even if I could afford to pay cash. You could adopt a whole village in Sudan for less.

"What's the street number again, Tiffany?" I asked.

She immediately answered, "238."

I spotted it. There was a heavy iron gate in front. I drove by slowly and then pulled over down the street.

When I write action adventures or action thrillers, I have days to figure out a clever way the protagonist gets through a gate like that. But in real life, which

I had to keep reminding myself this was, I had to change my plan or come up with something quick. Since there was no way I was getting apprehended before I talked directly to Katie Portman, I knew a strategy had to be formulated instantly. A strategy that would work and get *Jane Blonde* into her hands.

"Any ideas of how we can get through that fence?" I loved collaboration.

Nobody said nothing. Great. How ungrateful can hostages get? I've spared their lives. They should be eager to share their creative ideas.

Then Fifi spoke up. "We could tell them we are the pool service or TV repair."

"You've been seeing too many Steven Seagal movies, Fifi," I said. He looked hurt and pouted.

"You could say you're delivering a script for Nevison." Tiffany sounded proud of her pitch. David glared at her from the back seat.

"Wouldn't she call her agent about that?" I asked.

"I don't think so," Tiffany replied. "We deliver scripts to her all the time. That's how I know her address."

David could contain himself no longer. "Tiffany, just shut it. And what are you doing delivering scripts to Katie Portman?"

I glanced in the rearview mirror to see Jason suppressing a grin. I was beginning to like this guy.

"It was only once, when Bambi had to get her nails done."

The Sisterhood of Those Who Can't Afford Beverly Hills Manicures But Get Them Anyway was tight.

"And you were out of the office, why?" David demanded.

Tiffany squirmed in the seat and said quietly, "I was on my lunch break."

"Lunch break?" David shrieked. "You don't get a lunch break."

"It was a Friday. You'd left for Vegas already."

I turned to look at David just as he snapped his head in Jason's direction.

Jason shrunk away as if he was expecting to be hit and said, "I didn't know."

"She doesn't get a lunch break?" I asked David.

He sort of snorted and replied, "She's an assistant," saying the word like he meant *leper*. "Assistants don't get lunch breaks. They can order in and eat at their desks if they have time. But Tiffany cannot drive all the way to Bel Air to deliver scripts for another agent."

"I only did it once." Tiffany studied her broken fingernail, running her thumb over the jagged edge and continued, "Or twice."

I eased the SUV up to the call box in front of Katie Portman's gate and pressed the red call button.

As we waited for a response, I studied the black wrought iron gate. It was an ornate design and had been covered by black metal sheeting on the other side, concealing the view of the house. Too many tourists with star maps congregating at the gates, hoping for a view of America's sweetheart actress, no doubt.

I pushed the button again. What if no one was at home? What if Ms. Portman was in Europe or in Africa feeding starving babies? I knew she wasn't supposed to be shooting a movie currently, because she had taken a much-needed one-month rest. This was reliable human intelligence, or HUMINT as the professionals say, according to a casting director friend.

Finally, a somber female voice came through the speaker.

"Yes?"

"I'm here to deliver a script to Ms. Portman from Nevison," I said.

The video camera was aimed straight at us. I smiled as charmingly as possible. The camera rotated toward the back of the car. I glanced back to see Fifi waving out the window.

"Who are the others?" The voice challenged.

"Agents. We're on the way to lunch."

The gate shuddered and then slid open. I guided the SUV up the drive and parked in front of the Spanish Colonial Revival mansion. It was probably built in the 20s for some silent film star.

CUT TO THE PAST:

Beverly Hills.

After being in LA for a year and depleting my piggy bank twice, I was forced to learn a little about the local architectural style when I took a job with a new homes magazine.

It was a startup publication called *Coastal Style* and an old friend was the publisher. He wanted me to return to Florida to design and create the magazine for him, but I couldn't give up on my mad chase for the Hollywood gold.

We worked out an unusual deal. I would stay in LA and edit the magazine from 3,000 miles away. Internet and e-mail made arcane employment arrangements like that possible. I would work on the magazine in the mornings and write my ball-busting screenplays in the afternoons.

The magazine was my baby for about a year. My staff was in Orlando and we worked out a brilliant schedule. It was lunchtime in the Sunshine State when I got into the office at nine in my Beverly Hills apartment. My psychic assistant, Beth, had already completed her list of things to do I sent the night before and was ready for more.

Coastal Style did well and my publisher eventually sold it to Southern Progress, a company that published *Southern Living* magazine. They were a division of Time Warner. The magazine was sold on newsstands all over the country.

Why didn't I take the stock offer when I first started? I had seen plenty of magazines go belly up. I wanted a fat salary rather than take the gamble that a mega-giant like Time Warner would buy the publication. Sometimes you win, sometimes you slash your wrists.

I got a quick education about California home designs and built up a war chest of rent money from editing the magazine. The cash took me through six months of LA lifestyle. Then I ran out of bank account again.

BACK TO THE PRESENT:

Bel Air.

The Portman villa had a curved façade and looked like something you'd find in Venice with wrought iron on the windows and chipped layers of various colors of painted stucco on the walls.

I parked the car on the glazed pavers near a fountain surrounded by tropical lilies.

The rushing water from the fountain drowned out any unpleasant traffic noise drifting up from Sunset.

"Everybody out," I ordered, as I took off my bulletproof vest, flung it into the driver's seat and picked up the gun.

Everyone piled out. Tiffany was transfixed by the elegance of the villa.

"It looks different when it's not raining," she said, forgetting to close the car door. "Wow."

"Will we see Katie Portman?" Fifi asked, straightened his red valet vest. "I'm her biggest fan."

I motioned for everyone to go up the steps, struggling to focus on my mission and not the grandness of the abode. It was exhilarating to be hobnobbing with the Haves, especially since I'd been a card-carrying Have-Not for so long.

"No talking," I warned them as we congregated at the massive carved wood front door on the terrace. I swung the weapon around to the small of my back, concealing it as to not unnecessarily excite whoever opened the door.

The owner of the voice from the squawk box at the front gate, a young woman in yoga pants and a well-fitting T-shirt, answered the door. She wiped her hands on a dish towel and reached out for a script. For once in my life I had no script.

"My instructions are to personally hand-deliver it to Ms. Portman," I said insistently.

Ms. Yoga Pants studied my posse suspiciously and said, "Where's the script?"

Her eyes squinted up as she saw there was no script.

As I pulled the MP-9 from behind my back, she lunged at the door to close it. I leapt forward, stopping the door with the barrel of the MP-9. Yoga Pants struggled to get the door secured, but an inch of gunmetal was between her and safety. I will say she had remarkable upper body strength for a skinny little broad.

"Call 911," she shouted, apparently to someone inside the house.

I planted my boot on the door and shoved it open, knocking Ms. Pants to the wooden floor.

"Inside." I motioned my entourage through the door. Quickly scanning the foyer, I could see no one dialing 911. Either someone darted into another room to make the panic call, or no one was there when the command was issued.

We gathered in the small vestibule. I closed the door.

Ms. Yoga Pants leapt up from the floor. "What? Are you stupid or high on something?" she asked as she flicked her curly bleached white blond hair off her face. "You can't just come in here like this."

I was in the home of one of the most bankable movie stars in Hollywood with four hostages, no, make that five, and maybe someone making a call off camera that would spoil my day.

"Where's Miss Portman?"

"She's not home." Ms. Yoga Pants betrayed her reply by glancing down a hallway to what looked like a kitchen.

"Let's go."

I escorted the group past a sitting room with 20-foot-high ceilings, silk drapery and antique tapestries on the wall. Fifi slowed, admiring the décor. "*Madre de dios*," he muttered.

Glancing back, I said, "Hey, this way, sport."

Fifi wandered along with Tiffany, mouth agape at the splendor, past the grand stone staircase, down the hallway lined with Italian paintings.

As we passed the Euro-style dining room, Fifi gasped and stopped. There was a dining table for 20 in the middle of the room under a massive wrought iron chandelier. One of the walls featured a mural of the Northern Italian countryside that looked like it had been painted hundreds of years earlier, with paint peeling away from the surface in strategic places.

> *Hell-A Rule #22: If you've got it, spend it. Even if you don't have it, spend it. Never live below your means. Forget about keeping up with the Joneses. Mow them down with your square footage, extravagant taste and excessive debt.*

I shoved Fifi forward and he stumbled down the hallway to the kitchen.

It was astonishing. As traditional as the other rooms were, the kitchen was all so Now. Stainless steel restaurant-quality appliances, custom pecan cabinets, dark greenish marble counters, can lighting in the 12-foot ceiling, drop pendants over the island and enough Le Creuset to open an outlet store.

Oh Lordy, could I do some cooking in this baby. In a glass-doored cabinet, they even had a red KitchenAid with all the attachments, including a pasta maker. It reminded me of a fresh pumpkin ravioli recipe I'd been dying to try. If only I had about two hours alone in this place.

On the counter there was a platter of fresh veggies and hummus, roasted olives, exotic fruits half peeled and other yummy-looking fusion dishes.

No one was making a phone call. Ms. Yoga Pants must have been faking the "call 911" order, hoping it would scare us off.

"Wow, this is beautiful," I heard Tiffany say. Through the massive windows I could see Katie Portman lounging by the sparkling pool, sipping a smoothie.

Fifi saw the star and squealed, "Oh, my heavenly God, it's her!"

"Quiet," I scolded him.

Fifi whispered to Ms. Pants, "Are you her friend?"

"No. I'm her personal assistant, macrobiotic chef, yoga instructor and life coach."

Talk about a hyphenate. Ms. Pants had the writer-directors beat.

Ms. Pants eyed her fellow hostages and said snootily, "Who are you people?"

Fifi extended his hand to Ms. Pants, "Fidel Bartolo Javiero Rafael Estevez. My fans call me Fifi."

Ms. Pants didn't shake hands but she nodded to Fifi. "Pamela."

Was Pam afraid of catching something? Whatever the reason for not pressing the flesh, it hurt Fifi's feelings. That boy had to grow some skin. His nerve endings were exposed in full view of any heartless sadist that cruised by.

He withdrew his hand and turned his attention to the fruit on the counter.

He nabbed a chunk of papaya and popped it into his mouth. Pammy scowled at him. At least Fifi was good at petty revenge.

A floor-to-ceiling glass cabinet of handblown champagne glasses captivated me. I stepped up to the cabinet, admiring the variety of designs, apparently created by the same craftsman.

CUT TO THE PAST:

Hollywood Hills.

The only other time I'd seen anything like it was at Robin Wright Penn's mother's house. My girlfriend from Brentwood invited me to a girl's night party there. It was one of those Hollywood soirees you heard rumors about afterwards and you were sure someone's publicist had made up. But that night I was there to witness how LA elite pampered itself.

When we arrived, we were met by an armed security guard. After checking his guest list, he invited us in. Robin's mom greeted us warmly and apologized for the muscle at the door. Her daughter and her son-in-law, Sean Penn, had had a spat recently. She had gotten involved somehow and felt she needed a doorman in case trouble showed up. Sadly Robin and Sean divorced a few years later, eliminating the need for artillery on the porch.

Robin's mother led us to a kitchen cabinet full of handblown champagne glasses, all one of a kind. Endorphins spurted through my brain, a kind of Pavlov's dog effect. Where there were expensive champagne glasses, there had to be expensive champagne. I stood there, spellbound by all those glittering glasses. I imagined they were a metaphor of how my life would be from that moment forward.

The evening was jammed with champagne drinking, noshing and gossiping. Robin's mom brought in a salsa instructor from Rio and a hair stylist from Paris. We learned a few steps and got new dos. That party became my new benchmark. I dreamed about living in one of those mansions in the hills and giving parties where I pampered guests with evenings of champagne and makeovers.

BACK TO THE PRESENT:

Bel Air.

"What the hell is going on here?"

I turned from my champagne dreams to see Pammy pointing at David and Jason's belt contraption binding them together. She was looking at Tiffany, as if to accuse her of something criminal.

"I don't know anything," Tiffany shrugged and said. "I'm just an assistant."

"We are being held against our will," David said, glaring over at me.

"Excuse me?" Pamela needed clarification.

David gave it to her. "This deranged bitch," he hissed as he pointed a finger at me, "has abducted us."

David started to unbuckle the belts connecting him to Jason. Pamela began to back away. Fifi sat down on a stool and began eating Ms. Portman's lunch.

Things were quickly spinning out of control. Like a tropical storm turning suddenly into a Category 4 hurricane. Being from Florida, I knew from experience the situation could escalate into a Category 5 disaster with no warning.

I realized I was completely outnumbered by hostages and even with a submachine gun, I would have to have hypersonic, *Matrix*-motion reflexes if one decided to ambush me. I raised the MP-9 hoping no one had the guts to challenge me and my little friend.

No one did.

Pam glanced outside, where Katie Portman sat 50 feet away. One scream and this divine madness would be for nothing. Since we had driven through those iron gates, I had been formulating a plan. I needed to talk with Ms. Portman alone, writer to actress. But what about my entourage?

I scanned the huge kitchen and spotted a pantry with a partially opened door. The room was about the size of my guest room at home and lined with shelves of gourmet foods. It looked like everyone would fit in there comfortably. And there was plenty of canned pate for a party.

"Is there a key for the pantry?" I asked Pamela, who looked like she was ready to bolt.

"No." But her eyes betrayed her again, darting to a key on a hook beside the pantry door.

"Tiffany, see if that key will lock that door," I said.

Conditioned by months of David's barked commands, Tiffany obeyed. Tiff tried the key in the door. It fit. She handed the key to me.

"Everyone inside," I commanded, trying to sound tough.

Tiffany stepped inside, scanning the shelves of yummies as she headed to the back of the pantry. Fifi followed, sulking and making a little whiny noise of protest.

David stood his ground and said, "I'm not going in there."

I stepped toward him. He stepped back and Jason leaned away from him as far as the belts would allow, anticipating my retaliation.

"You have a low pain threshold, remember?" I reminded him.

Jason pleaded with David, "Don't screw with her, Dave." Jason edged toward the pantry with David in tow. "Come on. This will be over soon."

My two agents resigned themselves to taking their chances with the pate rather than a rabid writer with a submachine gun.

I realized that while I was herding my captors into the pantry, Pammy had been edging toward the open doors to the pool area. I swung the MP-9 her way, squinting my eyes trying to look tough, shaking my head warningly.

"How good is your health insurance?" I asked Pam. She didn't answer. "And do you have worker's comp?" I continued.

Pam considered this a moment and then decided to take her chances in the pantry. She gave attitude every inch of the way through the door and said, "She doesn't keep cash or her good jewelry in the house."

"Quiet." As I closed the door, my screenwriter's logic kicked in.

"Wait. Do you have a cell phone?" As I said it, I realized that if Miss Yoga Pants did, she sure as hell wouldn't admit it.

I held my hand out. "Give me your cell."

A moment of dead air, then Tiffany to the rescue, "You better do it. She's psycho."

Pammy stalled a moment and then reluctantly fished a tiny flip phone out of her pants pocket.

"Just got it yesterday. It can even make a film." Pamela aimed it in my direction, shooting digi-footage.

"Hey!" I held my hand between the camera and my face. Then I darted in and grabbed her new toy.

"But I have personal photos on it."

Fifi pushed by Jason and David to suck up to Pamela, asked, "Pictures of celebrities? Do you know other movie stars?"

"Kevin Costner. And Katie, of course."

Fifi took a deep breath, rolling his head to the side and said, "Oh, my Lord. Kevin Costner. I'm his biggest fan. How well do you know him? I wrote a script for him."

Hell-A Rule #23: If you live in the LA metro area, you are required to write at least one script expressly for Kevin Costner. Or if you happen to adore Tom Hanks, it can be written expressly for Tom Hanks. The town is populated by writing whores.

I was no exception.

I stepped out of the pantry, slammed the door shut and locked it.

Alone again. An instant calm came over me. My responsibilities as jailer were relieved and I was good to go. They were out of my sight. I was out of my mind. I stood still a moment, listening for police sirens or helicopters. Nothing.

Gathering my wits, or what was left of them, I pondered exactly what I would say to Ms. Portman. I knew this was a turning point in my career. It would go well and life would change dramatically for the better. Or something much more unfortunate would happen.

CUT TO THE PAST:

Beverly Hills.

I'd seen close up what the right element could do for a project. An element is anyone who helps get the movie made, especially a bankable actor, actress or a desirable director. Deals in Tinseltown come together quickly and fall apart with equal speed, depending upon talent.

A girlfriend and I met Wes Craven at a reception after one of his *Nightmare* movies. Within two weeks she had secured a desk in his office and he was producing a horror movie she'd written. All because she was bright enough to spot the next hot young director out of Britain and attach him to her script. Craven wanted to be in business with the young director, New Line wanted to be in business with Craven and so a movie was born.

Problem was, nobody read the script. Unbelievable, but true.

New Line brought the director over from London and with everyone, including Craven, sitting in the studio head's office, a New Line development dog mentioned they only had one note: they didn't like anything about the story. My friend ignored the severity of the moment and guaranteed she would get input from everyone and deliver a new draft in two weeks. She spat out ideas for a new page-one script in a rapid-fire, desperate attempt to keep the deal from exploding in her face.

The New Line prezzie asked the director what he liked about the script. When he said, "Nothing," and fled the room, the deal crashed and burned.

The director was so humiliated he took the next flight to Heathrow. Suddenly Craven's staff urgently needed the extra office and my friend was exiled to the kitchen table of her Pasadena apartment.

Hollywood deals are as fragile as nitro.

BACK TO THE PRESENT:

Bel Air.

Having Katie Portman do the lead role in *Jane Blonde* would assure the film got made. Attaching a valuable element through a kidnapping plot was unorthodox, but probably not unprecedented. A good first impression was crucial. It was like auditioning for a top-rated reality show. You nailed it and went to Hollywood, or you embarrassed yourself in front of millions of people, and dragged ass back to the trailer park and your old job at the Wal-Mart warehouse.

I eyed the fresh hummus on a platter surrounded by toasted whole-wheat pita chips and colorful baby vegetables. I clipped Pammy's cell to my SWAT belt and laid the MP-9 on the counter. I picked up the tray, said a little prayer and headed outside.

Crossing the magenta bougainvillea-covered veranda, I rehearsed what I would say. By the time I was to the pool, I had it worked out, sort of.

Katie looked up as I approached. She smiled that $15 million smile and said, "Hi."

"Hey." I thought a southern-fried accent would put her at ease.

I sat the tray down on a teakwood table beside her chair.

Katie Portman was one of those effervescent stars that always seemed *on*. Even without makeup she was stunning. A Park City baseball cap covered her natural blond hair. She wore a bright pink tank top over black cotton shorts. There was a tiny sparrow tattooed near her right ankle.

She eyed me with a friendly curiosity.

"Thanks. Where's Pamela?"

"Oh, she's on a call with Kevin. I'm Liz. I'm here for a meeting about *Jane Blonde*."

Katie grabbed a tiny yellow squash, dipped it in the hummus and popped it in her mouth. As she chewed she looked like she was searching her cranial database for the appointment.

I was scanning my own database for my next line.

"Jane who?"

"*Jane Blonde*, my script Nevison sent you. I'm Liz Bradbury, the writer."

"Huh." She popped another infant veggie in her mouth.

I gazed out over the long, glistening pool to a waterfall at the end. There was an open-air bar and BBQ grill under an awning attached to a guesthouse that was designed like a miniature Italian villa beyond the pool. The whole backyard reminded me of Key West. Southern California and South Florida share a lot of the same vegetation: palms, tropical flora and washed-up movie stars. In Katie's case she'd have a good two years before she would be a has-been.

"My agent, David Isaacson, set our meeting up through your agent a month ago."

"And I said to come to the house?"

"You said 238 Oracle Canyon Road."

"Huh. I must'a totally spaced out. And you said the project is called *Jane Blonde*? I'm sorry, but there are so many scripts. Remind me who the producer is."

"Gale Grazer." I was lying, although Ms. Grazer's production company took it to five studios, so she must have liked it. And she would have been the producer if one of the studios had bought it or Katie Portman had said yes.

"Oh, sure. Remind me what the story was about. Sorry."

"A super-spy named Jane Blonde, like James Bond's illegitimate daughter, although, of course we can't say that. Copyright infringement. And her assignment is to protect the British Prime Minister from a kidnapping attempt, which she does. But then three of the G-8 finance ministers are abducted and Jane has to rescue them."

"Awesome." She looked as if she meant it.

"It's set in London, New Zealand and Antarctica."

"New Zealand? I definitely want to go to New Zealand. So can I read the script?"

What was I going to say? No, sorry, you stupid bitch, you should have read it when I thought you got it two months ago, time's up, you've ruined my life, you can't read it now?

"Are you sure you didn't get it? My agent said he sent it to you two months ago. And he said you said you didn't like it. Maybe you got it, but didn't actually, I mean..."

Oh God, I should have plotted this conversation out better, at least my part. I'd fallen in a logic hole and had to dig my way out. If she was supposed to have read the script and said it wasn't her cup of tea, why did my agent set up a meeting for today? My mind shifted into hyperspeed trying to figure a believable explanation.

"You've probably heard all those lies about me not reading scripts. Well, they're true. God, I don't sound like the last George Bush, do I?" She laughed and continued, "What I mean is, I don't read bad scripts and most of the crap that's sent to me is crap. I don't mean your script is crap."

It went right past her, the logic hole. Maybe she wasn't listening.

I said, "So maybe my agent sent it, but..."

"No. I'm sure. *Jane Blonde*...I, like, *love* that title. I would definitely remember. I would have read it. Filming in New Zealand would be a blast."

I had to go to the pantry and shoot David Isaacson in the heart.

"Ah...Could you excuse me just a moment?" I spun on my heels, rage overtaking my sensibilities.

"Ladies room is through the kitchen on the left," Katie shouted after me as I raced across the veranda and into the kitchen.

My hand trembled as I tried to get the key in the pantry door. It clicked in and I jerked the door open.

"Liar! Liar!" I blurted out, spraying spit like a boxer getting pounded.

David, Jason, Tiffany, Fifi and Pammy all fell back in unison. All looking guilty as charged.

"David Isaacson, you are a deceitful bastard. You never gave *Jane Blonde* to Katie Portman. You said you did, but you didn't."

David looked bored. "So?"

"So? What do you mean, *so?* We agreed that the strategy was to get an actress attached. You told me you sent it to Katie and she didn't like it. But she said she never saw it. I thought you had integrity. I thought you were an honorable man."

At this point both Jason and Tiffany burst out laughing. I ignored them and continued, "I trusted you, David. But you lied to me. Never, ever lie to me."

Hell-A Rule #24: Lying is not really lying. It's justification improv. The movie business revolves around making up stories. Real life in Hollywood is no exception.

I felt my face growing warm. My breathing was shallow and fast. I rarely lost my temper because I was afraid I'd lose myself in the process. But all I could think of was grabbing David's throat and squeezing. That was better than grabbing the MP-9 and squeezing.

"By the way, another little sandspur — you put Matson & Abner up for my writing assignment over at Sony. That's, that's unethical."

David shot a cynical look at Jason. Like, why do we have to endure these demented writers?

"Don't you disrespect me," I ranted. "I'm tired of people disrespecting me."

David laughed, "You're a writer. Get used to it."

There was a moment when all thought was suspended. The only thing I was aware of was my face was on fire. Then I launched into the pantry and grabbed David by the throat.

"I hate liars. I hate men who lie to me. I hate this business."

David tried to push me away, but I had a death grip on him. He was going to pay for every snub I had ever felt from every snob who'd snubbed me in Hollywood.

He'd pay for the action movie producer who called me in for a pitch meeting at a private Beverly Hills cigar bar. But instead of listening to the pitch he screamed on the phone at someone with Disney about getting his freaking money. During our 45-minute meeting I tried to tell the story in between increasingly hostile phone calls. By the end of the torture session, I was certain he had not heard a word of the pitch that took me two weeks to research and write. I hoped he never got his freaking money from Disney.

"Hey, hey, you'll hurt him." Pammy grabbed the little finger on my right hand and twisted. My right hand came off David's neck just long enough for David to gasp, catching his breath.

As he sputtered, I thought I heard him whisper, "I'm sorry." But it was probably my imagination. All Hollywood agents are certifiable sociopaths. They have no regrets because they have no feelings.

I backed out of the pantry and bumped against the kitchen island. I teetered there cooling down. The pantry inhabitants stood there staring at me cooling down, all except David, who collapsed coughing on a crate of expensive imported fruit.

At that instant, I realized that Jason was a good five feet from David, obviously no longer tethered by their belts. Somebody had been a very bad boy and I was sure it was David.

In the distance I heard a voice, "Can you bring a lemonade when you come back out?" It was Katie, still by the pool munching on beta-carotene.

I took a breath and shouted back, "Sure. No problem."

I slammed the pantry door shut, locked it, and grabbed a bottle of French lemonade from the $13,000, stainless steel, double-wide, Sub-Zero fridge.

As I headed back outside with the lemonade, I composed myself by repeating one of my many affirmations: "I'm calm and happy and standing straight. I'm losing weight and looking great."

Miraculously, I became calm and happy and started standing straight as I walked out to the pool. The losing weight part I would work on later.

Katie was on her cell phone, studying me with a new curiosity.

"Oh, no problem, really. Yeah, sure. See ya soon," she said to someone at the other end.

I handed the lemonade to Katie. She flipped open the swing top and took a long sip as I sat down next to her. She stared out across the pool to the waterfall a vacant moment.

The faint scent of jasmine drifted by on a Santa Ana breeze. I scanned the landscape and spotted a healthy jasmine plant blooming near the entrance to the guesthouse.

Then Katie looked over at me with a frightening seriousness and said, "You didn't have an appointment, did you?"

I felt myself falling into a wormhole of lies. I struggled to maintain my balance, but I reeled with psychological vertigo. This was it. I was hitting the wall. The police were on the way. My head was shrinking.

"I…It's a long, sad story," I mumbled as I felt myself go all soft and mushy like overcooked squash.

"Right." I could see Ms. Portman was getting irritated.

I had to cowgirl up.

The true confession floodgates opened and a torrent of words poured out.

"I'm sorry. My agents screwed me over. I write. That's what I'm here to do. And those bastards promised everything and delivered nothing," I blubbered, fighting back tears.

I didn't do tears. Like I said, I hate women who go all weepy and boo-hoo all over themselves. But now at this moment, I felt like a guest on the "Jerry Springer."

To avoid crying, I focused on the Italian tile along the pool's edge. I studied the deep blues and yellows and reds, redirecting my mind to exterior things. It was a trick I'd learned from my Scientologist friend.

When I regained my poise, I continued, "What am I supposed to do, just lie down? Well, screw that. I am not lying down for any vermin agent. I will not be intimidated by wackadoodle whores in Armani, at the studios, at the agencies or on the set. Not now. Not ever. I am the creative source. I am the writer. I am the keeper of the flame."

I took a deep breath and sighed, "I am the underdog."

Katie looked at me sympathetically and said, "I love underdogs."

Then she smiled the most angelic smile I've ever beheld.

Chapter Nine

INCOMING ELEMENTS

Bel Air, Present.

"So he told you I read your script? Your agent, I mean," Katie said.

My heart was still pounding from my underdog monologue. I flopped down on a chair near Katie's. Physically exhausted, emotionally vulnerable.

"Right. I hate when they lie. He could have just said he didn't want to send it to you or something."

"All agents do that crap, but they don't call it lying, they call it massaging the client." She laughed.

"If I'd needed a massage, I would have gone to Beverly Hot Springs."

"Don't you love that place? It's so totally retro." Katie dipped a tiny $3 eggplant in the hummus and chopped down.

Her cell phone rang. She checked caller ID and said, "Sorry. I have to take this."

She answered, "Hi, Geena."

I was unsure of what to do. I didn't want to appear to eavesdrop, although I really wanted to hear the latest LA dirt. I dipped a carrot in the hummus and pretended to admire the landscaping while trying not to sound like a goat eating turnips.

Katie laughed and said, "He's such a horndog. And every new show he's on, he thinks it'll win him an Emmy."

I got up and wandered over to a row of rose bushes in full bloom, taking care to keep within earshot of the conversation. I leaned over to sniff a coral-colored flower. It had no fragrance. Hollywood.

Katie turned away from me and lowered her voice. I caught bits of the exchange. She asked advice about whether to take a certain movie role or not. And then I heard, "I don't care what anyone says, *Long Kiss* is one of your best films."

She was talking to Geena Davis. I was sure of it.

CUT TO THE PAST:

Hancock Park.

I'd met Ms. Davis at one of Shane Black's famous Halloween parties at his Gothic mansion. Shane wrote *Long Kiss Goodnight,* which hit the movie theatres that year, 1994. He was paid $4 million for that script.

He'd gotten $250,000 for *Lethal Weapon,* released in 1987, and $1.75 million for *The Last Boy Scout,* released in 1991. Shane was at the top of the writer's A-list in the early 90s, but he slid into anonymity when writer's block and depression ruled his Fremont Place address.

Shane and I were both on faculty for many of Sherwood Oaks Experimental College's seminars and retreats, talking about screenwriting to delirious writers much like me. I admired his success. He admired my prolific writing.

At Shane's party, a young woman sat down at a table with me and Fireball, my indie producer friend. She was dressed in one of those little kid's "sailor" outfits from the early 1900s complete with beanie and giant lollipop.

She looked vaguely familiar. Maybe she was a wannabe actress I'd met at one of the Women in Film breakfasts at Paramount.

Others sat down and started talking with Ms. Lollipop. I whispered to Fireball, "She looks like a young Geena Davis."

Fireball gave me a horror-struck look and hissed, "She is Geena Davis."

I took a big gulp of merlot. Here I had sat the last 10 minutes talking to Geena Davis and didn't even know it. Duh. I felt a sudden urge to find the nearest bathroom.

I leapt up, knocking my folding chair over. Everyone at the table looked up as I tried to recover, apologizing and flailing about like a female Woody Allen.

Then, in my embarrassment, I blurted out, "Anyone know where the ladies room is?" I got four blank stares, until Geena Davis stood up and said, "Follow me."

I'm not a short girl. The boots I wore made me at least 6 feet tall, but Geena was taller. We looked like two Amazons as we moved through the crowd, either that or two drag queens. Revelers moved aside for us.

She led me to the downstairs powder room, where there was a line of young beauties waiting to get in. We joined the line and Geena chitchatted about how I knew Shane. I hope I didn't say anything too stupid. Under the influence of wine and celebrity, I'll say whatever pops into my mind.

Like when we realized the line wasn't moving, I said, "Should we kick in the door?" Fortunately Ms. Davis found it hysterically funny. The two midget girls in front of us quietly left.

Quickly there was only one witch standing between Geena and the toilet when a bleary-eyed clown staggered out. The witch took a step toward the powder room, but spun on her heels, flipping a business card in Geena's direction. "You go first."

Geena flashed that dimpled smile, took the card and retreated into the bathroom. The witch shouted through the door to her. "Recommend me to the casting director on your next picture."

"Will do."

Even biological functions are bargaining chips for career advancement in the film biz.

BACK TO THE PRESENT:

Bel Air.

Katie flipped her cell phone closed and said, "I'm really sorry."

"No. No problem," I said graciously.

"I'm trying to decide on my next project and my friend, Geena, is kind of a mentor, really." Katie scooped up hummus with a cucumber slice and popped it into her mouth.

"So, you'll have Nevison send over your script?" she asked.

I had broken into Katie Portman's house, imprisoned hostages in her kitchen pantry, fibbed about having an appointment with her, and now she was forgiving me?

"So, you're okay with…ah, me being here and everything?"

"In this business, you have to step out of your comfort zone sometimes."

"You mean, your comfort zone or mine?"

Katie laughed. "I mean, I admire your spunk."

"Thanks."

"I'll just call Gale," she said. "Lyndsey will, like, bring your script over right now."

As she reached for her cell phone, my first impulse was to stop her. I hated for her to catch me in another semi-lie now that I was redeemed. But what would it hurt for Gale Grazer to know Katie Portman was interested in *Jane Blonde*? I was sure they'd still have the script among their pile of "almost-a-deal" screenplays.

"Sure. Why not?"

Katie hit one of the speed-dial buttons. She must know Gale and company well. Then I remembered she'd done a picture for them two years ago. I guess they were all still on speaking terms.

"Hi, it's Katie. Is she in?"

A moment went by, then she continued, "Gale, how's the cold? Oh, good. I told you that Ester-C worked miracles. Listen, can you send over *Jane Blonde*? For some reason Nevison never got it to me and I'm, like, dying to have a peek."

I held my breath, hoping Gale would remember the script and wouldn't question how Katie heard about *Jane* or why she wanted to read it. No one questions a star that can get a movie made. Also with talent like Katie attached, Gale knew every studio in town would revisit the project.

Almost any movie that gets made in Hollywood has had a twisted journey to principal photography. It's common for a script to be passed on by every studio in town, then become the subject of a bidding war once it's "discovered" by a star.

"Brilliant. See you next week for lunch." Katie made kissing noises and hung up.

"It'll be here in an hour. Have some hummus. It's organic." She rolled her eyes on the last word and then giggled. "I'm supposed to be on a diet."

Even though I had devoured two In and Outs less than an hour before, I was ravenous again. That's what stress does. Makes me eat. After tearing through half the hummus and vegetables, I sat back on one of the lounge chairs.

"What are you working on now?" Katie asked.

In Hollywood this is the same as saying, "How are you?" when you encounter a friend at the mall. You don't really want to know how the person is. You can see it in their face. They're happy or sad, overweight, depressed, suicidal, homicidal. You can see it, but you're not going to hear it, although you ask anyway. Everyone says the same thing, "I'm fine. How are you?" You say "I'm fine," although you're not. Nobody's fine except the Buddhists, Kabbalists and Scientologists, and even they have a bad day occasionally.

When someone asks what you're working on, you definitely don't want to say, "Nothing." So I told her about my new *Jane Blonde* script set in Cannes during the International Film Festival. Jane discovers a conspiracy that makes her the target of a secret international cartel of South American assassins.

"Wow, that sounds interesting."

"Well, I'm going to Peru to do the research and that'll be pretty cool."

Katie said, "Wow. I've always wanted to go to Peru. It's so spiritual."

"That's part of the plot," I said, thinking on my feet.

"Do you think I could have a little peek at the script when it's finished? I mean, if no one else has a first look or anything."

I wanted to leap up and do the happy dance around the pool but instead I turned the cheering down in my head to a soft "wa-hoo" and said, "Oh, sure. No problem."

I reeled with the headiness of knowing my next script was going to one of Hollywood's leading actresses for a read. It was a feeling much like eating a fat gob of wasabi on a spicy tuna roll or having Miramax say yes to a pitch.

You go out of the room in a spacey euphoria and hope you can find your car after you leave the building.

CUT TO THE PAST:

West LA.

One of those euphoric moments happened once on *The Tyree Legend* project I was working on with Bill Kelley. We had finished our outline for a film and created a strong pitch.

It was my first real pitch tour, one where you went into production companies on the studio lots and expected them to take you seriously. Bill's Academy Award got us some mileage and meetings with every prominent producer in town.

I will say it must have been a pretty powerful pitch since we almost had a fatality. We pitched to a development exec at a well-known production company whose assistant looked like a boy who had been kept in someone's basement for years—pale, nervous, and afraid to breathe.

I led the pitch off by describing the opening scene in graphic detail, ending with a young woman, skinned like a deer, hanging by her ankles from a tree.

I heard Bill say, "Son, are you alright?"

When I looked over at Basement Boy, he was slumped over on the sofa. I could hardly believe my eyes. He had fainted. Momentarily, the boy came to and popped back up like a Jack-in-the-Box ready to take notes again.

"Well, we won't be seeing that in the movie. Good Lord." The aging development director said of our horrifying opening scene. She looked indignant, like we had just suggested that she play the lead role in our next porn flick.

We figured it wasn't the right fit.

Bill's agent had scheduled 18 pitch meetings in less than a week. I learned the ropes from Bill during our mad dash toward another Oscar.

Hell-A Rule #25: Never bring personal firearms to the studio. They will be confiscated during the search at the gate and you will be arrested. Of course, the publicity could be good for your career, so it may be a wash.

Fortunately, Bill had left his six-shooter in his suite, so all the security guards at Warner Bros. found were empty ammo boxes. The excitement around the boxes prompted a call to a security supervisor who happened to be a gopher on "Bonanza" when Bill was a writer there. The supervisor remembered Bill, since Bill was the only above-the-line employee on the set who would speak to the young greenhorn. He let us onto the lot with Bill's promise of not shooting up the place.

We were near the end of our pitch tour and we didn't have a deal. We were getting worried when we got a bite from one of the best producers in town. He took us into Miramax to pitch and the studio exec said yes the minute we were finished. We were elated.

After our Miramax victory, Bill and I went to Trader Joe's and loaded the trunk with champagne and liquor, anticipating many long writing weekends at his ranch in the Eastern Sierras. Shortly afterward, Sean Connery's company heard we had been pitching him as an ideal actor for the film. Connery's development director called us in to pitch. We did and she loved the story. Then the producer who took us into Miramax said their directing partner would direct if Connery would star. We were giddy with our good fortune.

Shortly our celebration turned to wrist-slashing despair when Miramax's New York office put together the budget including hefty salaries for Connery and the director. The budget was over $60 million, way over Miramax's capabilities at the time.

As fast as the deal fell together, it fell apart. Woe was us.

BACK TO THE PRESENT:

Bel Air.

"Do you mind if I just get quiet a moment?" Katie said. "It's a thing I try to do after lunch when I'm not working."

"Meditation?" I asked her.

"TM. But I'm not very good at it," she admitted.

"I've been doing TM for…" Here's where I had to calculate the actual years and subtract 10. In Hollywood, anyone over 30 was exiled to an assisted-care facility.

"Let's see. I started TM when I was 17." That was a much safer tack. I didn't lie, but I also hadn't revealed proprietary information that could be damaging to my career.

"Wow. Who was your teacher?" Katie asked.

"I studied TM in my world religion class in my senior year in high school," I said and told her about my initiation into the concept of what you saw was not necessarily all you got in life.

CUT TO THE PAST:

DeLand, Florida.

Our class met in the cafeteria, so I used to go off into a corner and meditate. One day I was deep in trance and my body rose up off the chair, went through the roof and floated up into the sky.

Then my index fingers split opened, then my arms, and when that happened, a blinding light instantly flew out of me as my flesh ripped open. My body fell away and I disappeared into the sky or space or something. There was this sensation of blasting off in a rocket. It freaked me out.

Then suddenly I was back in the chair in the cafeteria. Dizzy and disoriented. I was sure everyone in the room had seen me float up to the ceiling and go through the roof. No one had. I pretended I was joking. I wasn't.

BACK TO THE PRESENT:

Bel Air.

Katie sat there, her jaw slightly open. "Oh. Wow. That's just incredibly awesome. You have to talk to my teacher. He tells about things like that all the time, except people don't think he's crazy. They think he's enlightened. You must be a highly evolved being."

Right. If I were a highly evolved being, I wouldn't be kicking ass and taking aim.

Katie leaned back and closed her eyes. The weather was perfect. About 72 degrees, a slight breeze across the water, a clear sky — well, as clear as the sky gets in LA.

We meditated. Twenty or 30 minutes I'd guess. It was blissful as it always is. Waves of ecstasy surging up my body. Then weightlessness. Then detached nothingness.

A loud thud came from the kitchen. Then another. I reluctantly opened my eyes. I saw Katie sitting up, her legs off the lounge.

"Pamela?"

Katie started to put her Gucci flip-flops on.

"Don't bother. I'll go see."

I hurried inside just as another thud came from the pantry. I grabbed the MP-9 from the counter and got the door open just as Pammy flung herself at the door. She hurled onto the kitchen floor, narrowly missing the stainless steel island.

She looked up to see the MP-9 staring down at her.

I heard something and spun around just in time to see Fifi trying to sneak out of the pantry, David and Jason right behind him. But good Tiffany was sitting in the back on a case of soy protein munching down a bag of stone-ground blue corn chips.

"I see dead people," I said, training the gun on the pantry door. The great escape came to a standstill with Jason and Fifi retreating back into the closet. David stood his ground.

"Now you, in the pantry." Since the gun barrel was a scant 12 inches from Pammy's perfectly waxed eyebrows, she complied.

"You've all been very bad girls and boys. Didn't I tell you to be quiet? If I have to open this door one more time…" I couldn't think of anything intelligent to say, so I said, "…it's going to look like a battle scene from *Braveheart* without the horses."

That really scared them.

David refused to back down and said defiantly, "I'm getting bored with your little hostage drama. I've got a full calendar of meetings this afternoon, so how much longer will this take?"

I lunged at him with the MP-9 and slammed the butt into his ribs. Some questions deserved answers. Some questions didn't.

David doubled over in agony. He staggered back into the pantry. Everyone else backed away as if the pain was contagious.

"If I hear a sound…" I imitated kids from 60s TV shows you see on TV-Land with imaginary submachine guns. Rat-a-tat-tat.

After everyone was safely locked up and warned against any further escape attempts, I headed back outside. Only I forgot I had the MP-9.

"What's that?" The look on Ms. Portman's face was priceless. I glanced down at the beautiful gun.

"It…appears to be a gun," I said tentatively.

Katie sat up in her chair and studied the weapon and said, "Where did you get it?"

"Burglars. That was what the noise was. I took this away from him, them, and locked them in your pantry."

I held the weapon by the end of the butt well away from my body like I was afraid of catching some kind of lethal disease from the gunmetal. Like I was gunaphobic. Like I'd never fired a round in my life. Would she buy the act? I wouldn't if I were her.

Hell-A Rule #26: Anyone hoping to work in the film and TV business must take acting lessons within 60 days of arrival in LA. Acting lessons aren't just for actors, they're essential to writers, directors, producers, or film crew members aspiring to become an actor, writer, director or producer. Finding the moment of truth within the lie you're telling increases the odds of people believing the falsehood.

She put her flip-flops on and headed into the kitchen. I followed.

This was so not going well.

"In the pantry?" She went to the pantry door and laid her ear against it. "No way."

She turned to me and in a whisper said, "They're whispering."

"They're dangerous."

Katie stepped away from the pantry door.

"Have you called the police?" she asked.

Just as she started for the phone, two things happened exactly at the same time. The front gate buzzer buzzed and someone inside the pantry said quietly, "Katie?"

I was closest to the pantry and heard the "Katie" part, but Katie was closest to the front gate buzzer and heard the buzzer part.

She went to the intercom/video camera. "Hugh! Come on in."

As she was saying this, I heard from the pantry, "Katie, is that you?" I hit the door with the MP-9. Everything got quiet inside.

Katie saw me hit the pantry door with the artillery.

"Just a warning. For the burglars," I said, trying to look convincing. One of the worst things about working in Hollywood for me was that I was a transparent liar. If I was ever forced into a corner and it was lie or die, I uttered the falsehood in a way that felt like I had a cartoon balloon above my head saying, "She's lying her ass off."

But surprisingly, she appeared to believe me.

"Can you call 911 while I go upstairs a minute?" Katie asked. "Makeup."

Well, first things last. Katie's priorities were clear. Vanity was No. 1, safety No. 2.

She took off for the cosmetics room.

I picked up the phone to see if she would call the police herself. But she didn't. At least not on that line.

I wondered who may walk in next. Hugh who? Hugh Hefner? Hugh Grant? Hugh Farrell? Was Katie dating Hugh Who? I didn't keep up with the gossip tabloids, so I was at a distinct disadvantage. Maybe Hugh Who was just a buddy. Dating in Hollywood could be dangerous. I knew from first-hand experience. I'd sworn never to date again just before I met Christopher. Two wacko experiences put me off men for months.

CUT TO THE PAST:

Beverly Hills.

Shortly after I arrived in California, I met a cute guy at an Independent Feature Project (IFP) west screening. The group is now called Film Independent, but I still call it IFP out of affection. We decided to go together to the next free film. No, I didn't know his last name. No, I didn't know where he lived. But I could describe him to police if the date went awry.

He arrived 15 minutes late to pick me up, which was a small minus in his column. As we were walking across the street to his car, he said, "Don't you want to know why I was late?"

As we climbed into his car, I said, "Okay. Why were you late?"

As he locked all the doors from his central driver's seat lock, he said, "Because I have a problem with road rage."

He cranked the engine of his tricked-out Z car and sped away. I laughed, thinking it was a joke.

"I'm not joking. I hate traffic. I can't stop dragging people out of their cars and beating the hell out of them."

At that point I was thinking of bailing out of the car, but my door was locked and the asphalt was moving by at about 50 miles per hour, in a 30 mile-per-hour zone.

We got to the theatre with no unnecessary violence. We watched the film with no unnecessary violence and I never went out with Mr. Rage again. I prayed I never accidentally tailgated him in traffic on the 405.

He was Date 1.

Date 2 was the marketing director for the world's most famous screenwriting seminars. I met him at one of Women in Film's Oscar night parties at the House of Blues on Sunset. It was an enchanting evening, and any man looked hot in a tux, especially a big guy with wide shoulders. We made out in the VIP room and he promised he'd call.

He did. We made a movie date. He was early by 15 minutes. After avoiding getting bitten by Aggie, he handed me a red rose.

"We really need to go. Now," he insisted, heading for the door.

I thought we had 45 minutes before the movie started. Even in the worst LA traffic, one can drive the one mile to the Century City AMC in say, 30 minutes.

He rushed me out the door and down the sidewalk. When we got to his car, I swooned. It was a 68 GTO. "Oh, my God. I love your car."

"I do, too." He beamed proudly, clicking a button to disable one of the three alarms he had installed on the classic.

I reached out to run my hand over the glittering finish.

"No. No. No!" Mr. Oscar grabbed my hand just as it touched the satiny smooth metal.

Suddenly the second alarm went off. It was an electronic voice with a Czechoslovakian accent: "Stand away from the car. Stand away from the car." Then the third alarm joined in: sirens, whistles, bells.

I started laughing. Mr. Oscar cursed, pressed buttons, stomped his feet, and circled the car in panic. I tried not to giggle. By the time he got all three alarms disabled, he was pissed. He didn't even open the car door for me. I jumped in just as he revved the engine and slammed the car into first gear.

Century City.

We raced to the Century City Mall underground parking garage in 15 minutes of total silence. Mr. Oscar leapt out, waited for me to clear the car, engaged all three alarms again and sprinted toward the escalators. By the time I got to the moving stairs, he was out of sight.

I got to the theatre box office. No Mr. Oscar. Huh. The ticket taker asked if I was Lisa because a big man in a hurry left a ticket for me.

"I'm Liz," I said.

He handed me the ticket unenthusiastically and I headed for Theatre 6.

As I walked through the lobby, I wondered if I should turn tail and run. This date wasn't going well. I wasn't sure I wanted to sit through a movie about falling in love and then have dinner with a man I was beginning to despise.

Oh, what the hell.

I found him in an empty theatre sitting in an aisle seat in the middle section. I crawled over him, planting myself in the seat beside him. It was too early for commercials, so we just sat staring at the blank screen.

After a few moments, he said, "Sorry. I have to have my seat."

"Your seat?"

"Yeah, I have a certain seat I have to sit in."

"You have to go 30 minutes early to get 'your' seat?"

"Right."

There was a long silence, then he confessed, "I'm blind in my right eye and deaf in my left ear, so there's only one seat where I can see and hear everything."

"Oh, I'm sorry about your disabilities." I wasn't sure if I was speaking into the good ear or the bad ear, so I increased my volume. "I didn't realize."

"And since I'm six five I have to sit on the aisle," he said looking at me kind of cross-eyed. "So you don't want popcorn or anything, right?"

Actually, I craved popcorn, lots of popcorn coated with trans fatty acids and a Diet Coke and another man sitting in Mr. Oscar's seat.

"I'll just pop out. Would you share a bucket of popcorn?"

He looked at me as if I had asked, "Would you share Bucket O' Goat's Innards."

I gathered from his non-response he wasn't interested in Bucket O' Anything.

I fled to the lobby for a Diet Coke, a small popcorn, and a quick escape to the open-air mall where I gobbled down the theatre snacks while waiting to be rescued by a friend I called on my cell.

I never heard from Mr. Oscar again. And he didn't hear from me.

After that I gave up on dating until Kira forced me to meet my destiny at The Stinking Rose Garlic Café.

Hell-A Rule #27: Never date anyone who works in show business. They're all nutcases.

BACK TO THE PRESENT:

Bel Air.

Just as Katie came back down the stairs, the doorbell rang.

I stashed the MP-9 in a cabinet. I heard voices and a moment later there was Katie Portman standing 10 feet away with Hugh Farrell, hot, hot, hot, since his new movie was No. 1 at the box office that last weekend. With Hughie baby was Unidentified Friend. That's what all the captions said below celebrity photos in the magazines if the celebrity got caught in the lenses with a noncelebrity.

If you're a noncelebrity in this town, you're a nonperson. You're one of the Unidentified. I had a recurring nightmare about walking down the red carpet on the arm of a movie star and the next day becoming one of the Unidentified. In the dream I shed my self-identity like a rattler shed its skin. Then a Beverly Hills Cop herded me into a corral with all the other Unidentifieds. I always woke up as the corral gate slammed shut.

"This is Hugh," Katie said. Everyone ignored Unidentified Friend.

I am totally not one of those women who goes all weak-kneed at meeting a gorgeous star, but Hugh looked better in person than on the big screen, and I was beginning to feel like hyperventilating. A day's worth of beard gave him a rugged, sexy aura. His ruffled blond hair looked like it had been styled by a Ferrari convertible.

As I shook hands, I realized Katie must have forgotten my name, "I'm Liz. Liz Bradbury."

"Any relation to Ray Bradbury?" Hugh asked in his gorgeous Australian accent.

"Actually, yes. I think he's my grandmother's great uncle's son." Did that make us distant cousins? I wasn't sure. I wasn't even certain that what my grandmother told me was true, but I liked to think it was. Her maiden name was Bradbury.

"Cool. You a writer, too?" Hugh asked.

"She's a terrific writer," Katie chipped in. "She's written a script for me that's, like, incredible. It's called *Jane Blonde*."

This was Hollywood. A star tells their other star friend that she loves your script and you're a great writer when she's never read one word you've written. It's all hype here and everyone is required to believe his own hype.

"*Jane Blonde*? Think I've heard of that. Female James Bond, huh?"

Hugh was fast.

"Maybe there's a part in it for a strugglin' actor like me." Hugh laughed.

I instantly realized we had most of the elements we needed to get *Jane Blonde* made: a successful producer and two stars. If only the right director would stop by for lunch.

Chapter Ten

THE MORE THE HAIRIER

Bel Air, Present.

Hugh Farrell tossed an In and Out bag to Katie and said, "Sounded like you needed a burger fix. Hell with all those baby carrots and field greens Pam's been feedin' ya."

Katie laughed a big snorting laugh and tore into the bag. "Cheeseburgers. Awesome," she said as she ripped open a wrapper and took a truck-driver-sized bite of a juicy burger.

For a tiny girl, under five foot seven, Katie was winning my heart. Most actresses on her level recorded every calorie and never ate baked goods, if hamburger buns could be classified as baked goods.

Before the Atkins rage, craft services, or caterers as civilians called them, loaded their tables on movie sets with doughnuts, croissants, Twinkies and cinnamon buns. Now it's cheese in any form, beef jerky, boiled eggs and cold cuts. Needless to say, the macrobiotic talent bring their own chefs loaded down with red quinoa, mini wheatgrass farms and probiotic, antioxidant elixirs.

Hugh and Unidentified Friend grabbed French fries. Munching away, Mr. Unidentified asked me, "Do I know your work?"

His accent was Aussie or maybe Kiwi. Even though I'd been co-habitating with a New Zealander for more than four years, I still couldn't identify the subtle difference in accents.

It had something to do with how "dance" is pronounced. The Kiwis say it the same way as the Brits, with a long "a" which ends up sounding like "dahnce." The Australian pronunciation is the same as the American, except for southerners, of course. My fellow rednecks — I use that term with great affection — say dance like it's ain't with a "d" on the front and a "c" at the end.

After Mr. Unidentified's question about whether he would know my work, Hugh shook his head and said to his friend, "Don't be such a dickhead. You sound so… Hollywood."

CUT TO THE PAST:

Beverly Hills.

After being in town a few short months, I had quickly learned everyone wanted to know the same five things within the one-minute window of assessment when they met another person claiming to be in the film or television business:

1) What do you do? (Translation: Can you do anything for me?)

2) Do I know your work? (Translation: Are you important enough for me to recognize your credits?)

3) What's your next project? (Translation: Are you working on something with important people I want to know?)

4) Where do you live? (Translation: How rich are you?)

5) What kind of car do you drive? (Translation: How rich are you?)

On occasion the two people will be on an even playing field, having worked on similar projects at the same level. More commonly, one of the two is in a much more elevated position in the business than the other. In which case, the superior player immediately recognizes someone across the room they must urgently bullshit. The inferior player desperately tries to get follow-up information like a business card, phone number or e-mail address.

Because no one in Hollywood has time to help anyone under them up the ladder of Hollywood success, business cards are always at the printers. If the underling is able to coerce the overling to jot down contact info, it's always accidentally transposed. But of course the superior player in one meeting is the inferior player in another.

BACK TO THE PRESENT:

Bel Air.

So when Hugh Farrell's friend asked if he knew my work, I considered lying, but didn't. It's too easy to catch a lie now that everyone has access to the Internet through their WPIDs (Wireless Privacy Invader Devices). Just go to the Internet Movie Database at imdb.com and check credits. Or Google the new acquaintance while they're gone to do coke in the bathroom and you'll find out what kind of person they really are. Of course, you can't believe everything you read on the Internet.

To answer Mr. Unidentified's question about whether he would know my work I said, "Only if you were an exec at Fox 2000 when they bought *Return of the Sweet Birds* or if you were a producer with 'On Hostile Ground.'"

" 'On Hostile Ground.' I think I've heard of that. Some Steven Seagal thing, right?" said Hugh.

"No, some John Corbett thing on TBS," I answered.

"John Corbett. Big Fat Greek Wedding, right?" asked Hugh.

"Right."

"TBS? Uh huh…television," said Unidentified Friend in a condescending tone. Hugh shot a warning glance his way.

CUT TO THE PAST:

Beverly Hills.

Television writing was a great way to set up a sweet retirement, if you could get the work. "On Hostile Ground" was a television movie that aired on TBS in June 2000. The MOW, or movie-of-the-week, was an original idea created by a writing partner in Florida and me. He worked for NASA, so I called him Space Cowboy. We developed the idea for a production company called, well, we'll call them TV Producer A to protect the guilty.

Cowboy was one of those talented, vulnerable writers who could only take small doses of the biz, so he only came to Hell-A for pitch meetings. Every day sensitive writers like him disappeared into the black hole of hurt feelings that hovered over every studio in town.

We developed a story of his with Producer A's development director, a.k.a. D-Boy. It was one of those cheesy disaster films that pulls big ratings and earns the writers a fat paycheck. It was called "Sinkhole" and was about a giant sinkhole that eats New Orleans during Mardi Gras. This was well before the real-life tragedies inflicted upon the Big Easy by Katrina and BP.

When we finished the pitch at our final meeting before going to the networks, D-Boy said, "Okay, good." That was about as close to "I loved it" as you're going to get.

Then he attacked two story points my partner had insisted on leaving in the pitch as ludicrous and uncinematic. Cowboy launched into a lecture on geo-reality, showing off his degree in geology. Two whole minutes passed before D-Boy stood up, leaned over his desk, inches away from my partner's horrified face and said, "If you go on like that at the network, they'll throw you out the window."

D-Boy sat down, threw out a couple more notes that I wrote down furiously and then said abruptly, "That's it. We're done." He showed us the door. "I'll meet you two tomorrow."

I scrambled up with my notes. Cowboy was speechless, his face an odd shade of I-hate-your-guts green. His genius went not only unnoticed but also disrespected. I towed him through the door.

Outside, in the bright light of humiliation, Space Cowboy stumbled toward my car. Instead of stopping at the passenger door, he lurched forward to a shady median and collapsed under a crepe myrtle tree.

"Are you sick? What's wrong?" I went to him and realized he was crying.

"He insulted me."

"So?"

"What does he know? Nothing. He's an ignorant ass," he howled.

Then he spewed the contents of his last meal, strawberry Pop Tarts and complimentary hotel coffee, all over the perfectly hand-clipped grass.

Hell-A Rule #28: Never let them see you barf.

I glanced back at the producer's building, praying there was no one in hysterics at the window. The glass was tinted black, so I couldn't tell.

Space Cowboy was close to being sucked up into the black hole of hurt feelings. I had to do something fast, so I said, "Well, I think it went amazingly well."

He stopped heaving and looked up at me in a bewildered daze, vomit drool dribbling from one corner of his mouth. "What?"

"Didn't you hear him say we were going into the network together? Tomorrow at two."

He looked at me as if I were speaking some alien language. Apparently, he had gone deaf after D-Boy's assault.

"You mean, they're buying it?" He wiped vomitus from his chin and struggled up.

"If the network likes it, yes."

A celebration broke out between the two of us.

We went into the cable network the next day. They loved it. They didn't buy it. No one was looking for a disaster movie then. Producer A's option expired. So did their interest. I wasn't surprised. Projects are hot, then they're not. It's Hollywood. You get used to it.

About six months later my agent at ICM called to mention that Producer A was considering optioning "Sinkhole" again. A day later Cowboy and I got option agreements to sign and return. But a funny thing happened on the way to the option. D-Boy, who by then had moved onto a new company, called my partner in Florida to say that Producer A had already sold the project to TBS.

Since Cowboy and I still owned the rights, I informed him that was impossible. But Cowboy, in a fit of paranoia, fired his entertainment attorney, hired a pitbull lawyer, and went for Producer A's throat, threatening to sign an option with D-Boy's new boss. As it turned out, Producer A had made a verbal deal with TBS through a larger production company before she bothered to secure another option, and D-Boy just happened to see a memo about it on someone's desk.

A lawsuit broke out between the two production companies and Cowboy and I ended up with almost $100,000 for a two-page story that went on to air as "On Hostile Ground." And we didn't even write the script.

BACK TO THE PRESENT:

Bel Air.

Katie, with her mouthful of yummy cholesterol from In and Out Burger, mumbled to Hugh, "She's an amazing writer. Really. Gale said so."

Wow. Gale Grazer said I was amazing? Amazing. I was reeling with an ego injection.

A crashing noise came from the pantry. Then a yelp of pain.

Hugh looked at Katie. Katie looked at me.

"Burglars," she said.

"Burglars? What're they doing in the closet?" Hugh headed toward the pantry.

"Waiting for the police." Katie wiped her mouth on a dish towel and continued, "I really needed a burger. All that vegan crap was making me spacey."

She emptied an order of fries out on the marble counter top, grabbed a bottle of ketchup and blasted them. "God, I love French fries."

Katie seized a handful of fries dripping in cholesterol, tilted her head back, opened her mouth wide and dropped about 1,000 calories down her gullet.

"I want to see these buggers." Hugh was almost to the pantry door.

Katie stopped him, trying to talk with her mouth full. "Hugh, they're criminals. Dangerous people. We're actors, not action adventure heroes."

Someone inside the pantry banged a hand on the door. Then came a male voice with a Mexican accent. "That sounds like Hugh Jackman. Or is it Hugh Farrell? Mary and Joseph, it's Hugh Farrell. You're my favorite movie star. I love you."

Katie laughed. "Hugh, I think you have a fan in the breaking and entering crowd."

"Let us out. She locked us in. She took us hostage. Help!" Fifi yelped.

"That's a good one," Katie said as she scooped up a handful of fries, grabbed a mineral water from the fridge and headed for the pool.

Hugh eyed me, looking not so convinced. I didn't like his suspicions. All it would take was one reckless cowboy to spring my prisoners and spoil my future plans.

"Police should be here any minute. Don't risk it," I pleaded.

Mr. Unidentified headed toward the pool, saying to Hugh, "It's none of our business, mate."

Hugh hesitated a moment, contemplating the pantry door. In my head I was running the same sentence over again: "Don't do it. Don't do it," as if telepathically I could persuade Hugh to give it up. Reluctantly, he followed his Unidentified Friend outside, quickly passing out of audible range of the kitchen.

"Help, Hugh. Help-p-p." More hands joined Fifi in banging on the door. Then other voices: "Help! Help!"

I was sure David wasn't one of the panicked prisoners. He wasn't about to let anyone see him lose his cool. Besides, one of the hostages may write a tell-all book some day, and David wasn't about to play the role of the scaredy-cat agent in that story.

I grabbed the pantry door key, unlocked the door and jerked it open. The hostages stepped back, startled by the sudden change in their circumstances.

Fifi pleaded, "We're starving in here. Can we order Chinese takeout?"

"You're joking, right?" I asked.

Fifi replied, "Okay, pizza is good."

"You're hostages. Hostages don't get takeout," I said, reminding them of the chain of command.

"Look, things are going very well here," I fumed. "Katie Portman said she would read my script. Hugh Farrell wants a role. So will you please just shut up and give me a break?"

David stepped forward. "I can set that up right now with Paramount. Half a mil against, say, seven fifty."

Everyone looked at David, then at me. This could be a crossroads in my career. He was right. Just the fact that two bankable stars were interested in your project could get a deal rolling at a studio. But did I want to have a lying, two-faced, swamp thing like David getting 10 percent or $75,000 of my deal after screwing me earlier on the same project? Well, maybe.

"And there's some chance I could get you a writing step," David said like it was a good thing.

That did it. My mind was made up. He wouldn't be making this deal for me if he were the last worm pig agent on the planet.

"I'll think about it," I said and slammed the pantry door closed.

CUT TO THE PAST:

Beverly Hills.

I wasn't the smartest screenwriter in LA, but Fox had paid my partner and I well to write a script. That should count for something. It got us into the Writers Guild of America union and propelled us into the elite ranks of "professional writers."

For an agent to say there was "some chance of getting me a writing step" was like saying, "Your script has been sold to friends I owe a favor to and they're hiring a new writer to screw you over."

No self-respecting writer would ever let her agent sell a script to a studio without requiring the studio to hire the writer to write at least one more draft. If a script was sold with no further writing required by the screenwriter, that meant the studio wouldn't have to contribute a percentage of the deal to the writer's WGA health fund insurance or pension fund. A writer needed health benefits. How else would psychiatric care be paid?

You have to learn to translate Hollywood-speak to a language you can understand. And even when an agent says all the right words like, "I'll get you another two writing steps on the deal," they may be fibbing. They all do it. It's a requirement. It's in their job description.

Shortly after moving to LA, I started hearing rumors that there was a super-secret class at UCLA called Lying 101 for Agents. They said it wasn't in the printed catalog or on the university's website public pages. But if you just clicked on the snake-in-the-grass icon in the upper right corner of the home page and entered the classified password, a whole schedule of covert curriculums bounced onto the screen.

There was supposed to be something for everyone—Creative Accounting for Studios, Producers' Strategies for Getting Free Rewrites, How to Steal Credits from Other Writers, and the popular How to Fake Being a Writer for Stars, Directors and Producers.

BACK TO THE PRESENT:

Bel Air.

You couldn't be a ruthless agent like David without letter grades in several of the rumored UCLA Covert Classes for Hollywood Players. Saying I'd think about the deal with Paramount left David with a $75,000 motivation to keep things under control in the pantry.

I closed the door and locked it. Just as I pocketed the key, the gate speaker buzzed.

I glanced through the window outside to see Katie, Hugh, and Mr. Unidentified diving into the pool all at once like a contest. They sprinted toward the other end of the pool. Actors thrive on competition, and I had to hand it to Katie—she held her own against the boys.

The gate buzzer went off again. I pressed the call button.

"Yes?"

"Gale Grazer here with a script for Katie."

"*Jane Blonde*, right? She's eager to read." No successful writer in Hollywood ever passed up an opportunity of self-hype.

"Right."

I buzzed her in and went back to the pantry and leaned close to the door and said, "Listen up. Gale Grazer is coming through the gate right now and…"

"Gale Grazer? I love her movies, especially the last one. Oh, that Governor Schwarzenegger. He's so hot," gushed Fifi.

"For God's sake, take a pill," I said. Jesus.

Hell-A Rule #29, a.k.a. The Cool Rule: Never be overly excited about anything. Maintain thy cool at all costs. The Cool Rule is suspended for pitches where foaming at the mouth and flailing of arms are recommended to communicate your passion for the project.

Fifi was so naïve to the Cool Rule, he was threatening to sink the boat, upset the apple cart and become a cliché.

Silence from the pantry.

"If you behave and we have a go-project, I'll make you all producers on the movie."

Fifi squealed. There were whispers and rustling around inside.

"Can you put that in writing?" It sounded like Tiffany. Smart girl.

"You don't trust me?"

No answer.

"Agents can't be producers," said David finally.

"You could open your own management firm and produce whatever you like."

It was true. Agents had been defecting to the management camp for years. Managers weren't regulated by the State of California Board of Labor the way agents were. Also, some managers didn't even take a cut of their client's income if they got producers' fees. It seemed to work out well for everyone, except managers weren't supposed to secure work for clients, but everyone knew they did it secretly.

"They've been talking about a management company." The ever-helpful Tiffany spilled her guts again.

There was the sound of someone smacking someone else. And then I think it was Tiffany who said, "Ow! I heard you talking about opening it and you're taking me with you."

CUT TO THE PAST:

Beverly Hills.

At the first Women in Film party I had attended a few years ago, I met a young woman who was an assistant to one of the most powerful lit agents in Hollywood. I learned a lot of shocking things from her. Not only about the lack of any kind of ethical or moral code, but also about how the town worked or didn't work.

A good example: When you thought you were talking in confidence on the phone to anyone, like an agent or producer, you were not. Ninety percent of the time, their assistant was on the call with you and you didn't know it.

There was a law regulating clandestine recording of conversations without consent, so how could they get away with other people secretly listening in on a confidential discussion?

That was getting into NSA territory.

My friend explained there were many reasons for the eavesdropping. Assistants had to follow up on commitments their bosses made to clients or associates. The more talented assistants even knew when to let a commitment "fall through the cracks" if their commander in grief was lying to a client. All assistants wanted to take their bosses' jobs someday, so what better way to learn the business than eavesdropping? Assistants liked to trade valuable information with other assistants.

Was I outraged? Nope, I saw it as an open door to a vast wealth of insider info.

I called it the Hollywood Assistants Underground. You could get anything done, except greenlight a movie, by knowing how to work the Assistants Underground. You could get coverage for any of your scripts from anywhere. You could find out what execs really thought of your pitch meeting. You could find out who was sleeping with whose wife, daughter, husband or civil union partner. If you really want to know who's running Hollywood, it's the assistants.

BACK TO THE PRESENT:

Bel Air.

"You can't buy *me* with promises of producer credits. When I get out of here, I'm suing." It was a female voice, so it had to be Pammy.

The doorbell rang.

Then from the pantry came the thud of a body blow, sounds of a struggle, squeals and chaos. Cans and boxes falling off shelves, glass breaking. Future producers overpowering an obstacle, no doubt.

I slammed my hand on the pantry door as I headed to the foyer. "Hey, hey. Quiet in there. Be good little hostages now. Today our lives will change."

Silence.

I hurried to the door and swung it open. Gale looked just like her pictures, only more animated. She had a mane of shiny brown hair that was long and silky like one of those shampoo commercials. She was dressed in a black suit with pants. Prada, no doubt. She charged right in without an invitation. "Hi, I have a script for Katie."

"You're Gale Grazer. I know your development director, Stephanie."

"Great gal. No longer with the company. Where's Katie?"

Gale raced to the living room, looking for Katie.

"Outside."

She marched through the kitchen to the pool, me in tow. Katie, Hugh and Friend surfaced in a dead heat from their race, all three gasping and laughing. Katie spotted Gale and pulled herself out of the water in one graceful money-shot motion.

"Gale. Hi! You brought it." She toweled off the chlorine and reached for the script.

"It may need a polish. We could put Shane Black on it. He's great with female action."

"But Shane doesn't rewrite other writers' scripts," I volunteered helpfully.

No one acknowledged my contribution.

Katie flipped to the last page to see how long the script was. A compact 110 pages brought a smile to her face.

The first thing anyone reading a script did was check to see how many pages they were going to have to gag down. Ninety to 110 was good. Any longer and it better be Oscar material. Longer than 120 and you might as well just write the novel.

She scanned page one and laughed a girlish laugh.

"Geez. I love how you started in mid-action right away. Cool."

"Thanks," I said, trying not to seem too humble or overly confident.

Suddenly Gale realized I was the scribe whose writing may need a Shane Black polish.

"You're the writer?"

I nodded. For about three seconds, Gale tried to puzzle out why on God's earth a no-name writer like me would be standing on the same real estate as Katie Portman, one of the most bankable actresses in Hollywood. Then she leapt forward with her hand thrust out for a shake.

"Excellent to meet you." She sounded like she meant it, just like everyone else in this two-faced town.

"Liz Bradbury," I said, crushing her hand with no mercy as we shook.

"Strong handshake."

I smiled, having heard that before.

One of the important things I'd learned from being a business owner was that a firm handshake speaks volumes about you. I hate people who extend their hand with a cold, wimpy handshake. Life's too short to do business with wimps.

Katie said, "She's Ray Bradbury's granddaughter."

Before I could correct her, Gale's look changed to "kinda impressed" and she said, "What a great script."

Right, except for the words you thought needed changing by an A-List writer.

"Thanks."

"Who's your agent?" Gale was sizing me up. She had taken *Jane Blonde* to five studios, but she didn't remember my name or which agent had sent her the script. I bet she'd forgotten Fireball was attached as a producer, as well. She'd be reminded by his option agreement when the deal started heating up.

"Ah, well, this morning I was at Nevison, but I'm thinking of making a move. I'm not really happy there."

Changing agents is a part-time job for any writer in LA. No matter what the reason, whether you're not getting the attention you need or whether your agent has given up on making fat commission checks on you, the thing you say is: "I'm not really happy there."

Of course, in this instance that was the safest tack since it was definitely true. Besides, what was I going to say, "I just shot up the place and my agents are in the kitchen closet?"

"I've got the purrr-fect agent for you," she said smiling like the Cheshire cat. "She just moved from CAA to ICM. I'll get you two together. You'll love her."

"Cool." Even though I was overjoyed to hear Gale Grazer was going to hook me up with an agent at one of the hottest agencies in town, I tried to seem bored.

CUT TO THE PAST:

Beverly Hills.

I had naively believed the first thing on my "Things To Do" list when I arrived in LA was to quickly find an agent to represent me. I believed it would be an easy thing to do. I also believed the earth was flat. All native Floridians do.

Hell-A Rule #30: You can't get an agent until you don't need one.

Agents weren't interested in representing what they called "baby writers." They had no credits and no deals pending or writing income flowing in. Agents wanted writers who were already banking at least six figures so their 10 percent commission would be substantial from day one of signing the writer.

Prominent producers didn't want to read scripts unless they were submitted through a decent agent. And unless you'd already sold stuff to such producers, you couldn't get a decent agent. What was a desperate writer to do? Start with obscure producers and indecent agents. Then work your way up.

With a major motion picture deal in the wings, a writer didn't "need" an agent because your entertainment attorney would do most of the negotiations, but agents were an essential decorative accessory for a successful film career, similar to one-carat diamond studs adorning two ears if you were female, or one in the case of male writers.

BACK TO THE PRESENT:

Bel Air.

Hugh and his Unidentified Friend came out of the water and plopped their firm, young butts on the Italian tile lining the pool.

Gale went over to Hugh, extending her hand. "Hugh, good to see you again." She disregarded Mr. Unidentified. Forget about exchanging DNA with someone who's not a valuable element yet.

Katie moved the party down to the far end of the pool near the guesthouse where happy hour began at the open air bar.

She sat down on the chaise lounge with a mineral water and started really reading the script. "This is, like, great. I love Jane Blonde. She's my kind of girl."

I had an instant feeling of well-being. An endorphin rush maybe. Or oxytocin blast, the organic chemical that floods the brain when you're falling in love. I was floating there in creative bliss with one of Hollywood's A-List stars close to saying yes to *Jane Blonde*. Nothing could break the spell.

Then I heard the whine of a police siren coming up the hill.

Chapter Eleven

LET'S GET OUTTA HERE!

Bel Air, Present.

Hugh and Mr. Unidentified were sipping beers and talking about going to Vegas for the weekend. Gale was on her cell with a studio. And Katie was submerged in the world of *Jane Blonde*, laughing as she got to the funny bits. I stretched out on a lounge chair, pretending to fit in.

Police sirens neared. No one seemed to notice but me.

CUT TO THE PAST:

Beverly Hills.

South of Wilshire, Down in the slums of Beverly Hills where I used to live, sirens whining, car alarms alarming, helicopters circling overhead, and gunshots popping off at the bank robbery on the corner became normal background din.

It was like living in a state of emergency 24/7. The chaos in my physical environment reflected the pandemonium in my inner world. Working in the film biz was like Trick or Treat year round. One minute the studio handed you a bag filled with a sweet movie deal, the next you were in the House of Horrors, noticing the bag had a big hole in the bottom.

It was around Halloween one year when Fireball and I were out on a pitch tour. I developed a story based on a book Fireball had optioned which was written by a Pulitzer prize-winning author. We found a studio creative executive, or CE for short, who loved the story. He gave us notes, of course. We went back with the revised story. He pitched it to the head of the studio. He said they wanted to make the movie if he could find co-financing. Sounds like a champagne moment, right? Don't hold your breath for sounds of corks popping.

Our CE said he was searching for co-venture funds, when he was mainly searching for his next hit of cocaine. His bipolar disease was made worse by the coke, and the coke was made more attractive by his bipolar disease. It was a vicious circle, and Fireball and I were at the heart of the cyclone holding on for dear life.

One day our movie was being greenlit, the next the deal was falling apart, only to be revived by our CE the next afternoon over lunch with a hot young actress. Ever wonder how crap makes it onto the screen at your local cineplex? Giant mood swings and drugs may have something to do with it. Oh, yeah, and Fear, with a big "F."

Fear, fed by rampant insecurity and fortified with widespread stupidity, drives almost everyone in Hollywood. Fear of not getting a callback after your best audition for the perfect role of your life. Fear of losing your cushy job at the studio because the first movie you shepherded through the system only made $30 million its opening weekend.

Fear of taking the most important writing assignment of your career and immediately getting a chronic case of writer's block. Fear of arriving on the set the first day of principal photography and having no idea what you want your movie to look like or how to direct your actors. Fear of your only A-List writer leaving you for the agent in the office next door. Fear of joining the legions of homeless on the Third Street Promenade in Santa Monica.

Things may look pretty from the outside, but inside Hollywood a quagmire of sludgy neuroses bubbles and boils. Even when you're on top, you're always secretly aware of how long the fall is into the bottomless crevasse of failure.

One wrong move and you plunge through the thin ice of show biz success. It can be agreeing to do a movie that looks like it could win you an Academy Award, but instead gets slammed by the critics and bombs at the box office. A couple of those kinds of miscalculations and you could be headed back to Kansas in a boxcar. Or worse, a body bag.

Of course, then there's what everyone comes to LA for: fame and eight-figure paydays. When the Good Witch of Serendipity smacks you with her wand and you are the hot item of the day, life is sweet—only better.

People recognize you on the street, which can be good or bad depending on what you're doing on the street. Ask Hugh Grant.

Your meals are free in certain restaurants, others you pay double and don't complain. You live in the Hills of Beverly above Sunset or on the Cliffs of Malibu overlooking the Pacific. You never have to stress about LA traffic because that's your chauffeur's job.

You get offered all the best roles, all the best directing jobs or all the best books to adapt. Everyone smiles a lot when you are around and laughs at all your moldy jokes.

You can have as many dogs or cats as you want. No city statutes apply to you or your $40 million mansion. It's like living in an embassy.

You can command the tony little shops on Rodeo to open at 2 a.m. if you have insomnia and are in acute need of a shopping-binge sedative.

You can have people fired or hired, promoted or demoted, grilled or killed.

God save Hollywood royalty.

To the millions who hope to become Hollywood royals, best of luck on the soul-shredding journey. And one word of advice: Never quit your day job. Never.

BACK TO THE PRESENT:

Bel Air.

The sirens whined to a stop somewhere on the street in front of Katie's mansion.

I sat up and looked at my new best friends. They were oblivious to the fact that LAPD was converging on the compound.

I thought I heard the faint sound of the front gate buzzer go off inside. Katie heard it too and put the script down. She glanced toward the kitchen.

"Where is Pam? She was there just a few minutes ago."

Katie started to get up.

"No. I'll take care of it." I jumped up and sprinted toward the kitchen door.

"Thanks." Katie curled back up with *Jane*.

Inside, the gate buzzer sent out an ear-piercing shriek. I slid to a stop in front of the intercom and punched the answer button.

"Yes."

"Miss Portman?"

"Who's this?" I said in my best Katie Portman voice.

"Los Angeles Police, ma'am. Someone called about a break-in."

My head snapped in the direction of the pantry. All was quiet. I noticed the doorknob turning, but the door didn't open. A small tap was heard, then, a whisper. "Hello? Katie?"

It was Pammy calling Katie.

I grabbed a perfectly formed, hydroponic tomato from the cook island and fired it at the pantry door. Beautiful ripe veggie flesh splattered all over the beautiful honey oak door.

Dead silence a moment from the pantry.

A voice came from the intercom speaker. "Miss Portman?"

I punched the answer button again. "What!?"

"I said, someone called about a break-in."

"Break-in. No. I mean, everything's fine. But thanks for coming out."

A moment of quiet from the intercom, then: "Do you mind if we come in a minute? Take a look around?"

"Excuse me? Are you calling me a liar?"

Silence from the intercom again. Then: "Ah, no, ma'am. But we have to come in since we got the call."

"Who called?"

"Do you have a Merna Rodriguez working for you?"

Merna? Who the hell was Merna? Was that who Pam was shouting to when we first arrived? Who knows?

"I'm a famous movie star. I have a lot of peeps working for me."

Hell-A Rule #31: In order to succeed in Hollywood, you have to have peeps. Peeps can be your agent, attorney, manager, publicist, personal assistant or psychiatrist. But the more peeps you have working for you, the higher up on the Hollywood Hill you are perceived to be.

Hell-A Rule #32: Law enforcement officers aren't impressed by your peeps.

"Yes, ma'am. We have to come in."

I glanced through the windows out to the pool where my new life as an A-List Hollywood writer waited. I turned back to the intercom where Cell Block A waited.

"Can you come back later? I'm in a meeting right now."

Silence from the intercom a moment and then, "Sorry. No, ma'am, we really have to come in."

If I let them in to look around, maybe they'd go away. That was a lame thought because as soon as Katie saw them, she'd say something about the burglars in the pantry and then another developing movie deal would go south.

"Ma'am? Buzz us in, please." The officer was sounding more commanding.

I was up against a wall, over a barrel, between a rock and a hard choice. If I thought things were screwed now with the wolves at the door, I'd find out how unscrewed they were if I didn't let the wolves in.

"Okay. Only two. I don't want the whole department tracking dirt into my new foyer."

Silence, then: "I'll be coming in with my partner."

As I buzzed the gates open, I heard more sirens headed up the hill. Oh God, let someone's mansion be on fire.

My brain buzzed with an adrenaline rush caused by danger approaching. I had to be calm. I had to figure out a plan, but all I could think about was Christopher. Would Christopher really leave me if I were arrested? Would he abandon me to the American prison system and take the next flight to New Zealand? Or did he love me enough to overlook this little mistake and stand by his deranged woman?

I grabbed my cell phone, turned it on and found 25 messages on my voice mail. I didn't even check. I knew they would be Christopher trying to talk me down.

I called his number at work. This time all I got was his voice mail. Damn. I tried again, but it went to voice mail again. I knew that Christopher rarely checked his messages, so I left one, thinking I could always say later that I really had tried to reach him.

"Christopher, hey honey. I've been thinking about what you said and have decided…" I hesitated because I hadn't decided anything. I continued, improvising as I went, "I love you and I'd die if you left me. I think things are actually going well. I mean, I'm at Katie Portman's house, and she really likes *Jane Blonde,* and there's a good chance we'll have a deal, because Gale Grazer and Hugh Farrell are here and things are looking very good, except that the police are coming now and I have to get off the phone."

"Who is it at the gate?" Katie's voice came from close behind me.

I spun around to see her at the terrace door. I ended the call to Christopher and flipped the phone closed.

My mind searched its database for a believable answer but it was stuck in a never-ending loop of the following three words: "I'm so screwed."

CUT TO THE PAST:

Florida Keys.

I'd been in the "I'm so screwed" place before and somehow, it always worked out. Like the time I was coming around a hairpin curve in my Formula

Vee, hitting the apex perfectly when a flash of red and white streaked by my left front wheel. In that instant I realized it was another car and we were in a head-on collision trajectory on Dead Man's Curve. "I'm so screwed" only came to mind a split second after we passed inches from each other. The slightest freak-out would have meant feeding tubes and a respirator for life or worse, if I was lucky.

BACK TO THE PRESENT:

Bel Air.

Staying the course worked then and I prayed it would work now.

I heard myself saying to Katie, "Police. Alarm went off. Probably a malfunction or something."

"What kind of alarm?" Gale came in the door, joining the girl talk.

Alarm. What kind of alarm? There was an answer there in the confusion called brain matter. "Fire alarm." The second it came out of my mouth, I realized it was a mistake.

"But I thought you said it was the police. Didn't you call them about our visitors?" asked Katie pointing to the pantry and beginning to looking a little suspicious.

All the breath went out of me. Caught in an avalanche of lies again. Should I just slash my wrists now or wait until later?

The front door bell rang. I glanced out into the hall leading to the foyer.

"Merna will get it. Didn't you say it was the police?" Katie asked again.

My flushed red cheeks always gave me away when I tried to lie. That Bible Belt upbringing rearing its ugly head again.

"And all liars shall have their part in the lake which burneth with fire and brimstone," Revelations 21: 8. Amen.

I heard footsteps dashing down the stairs, the front door open and a flood of loud Spanish jabber echoing off the marble walls of the entryway.

In 30 seconds my screenwriting career would be over and my potato-peeling career would begin if I didn't do something.

What would Jane Blonde do?

For the second time in my life, I had writer's block.

I could not think of one useful thing Jane Blonde would do in the same situation. Not one thing. My mind was vacant except for a primal plea bouncing around the void. The action-adventure cliché of all times, "Let's get outta here," was my only thought.

Too late. A male cop who looked like Vin Diesel in XXX came through the door followed by a female cop with some really bad plastic surgery, or maybe she'd been shot in the face.

"There was a call of a break-in?" the female cop asked.

Merna Rodriguez followed the cops cautiously. She was a short person with scared eyes. I think she was dressed in ill-fitting cast-offs from Katie. When she saw Katie, she crossed herself and said, "Mary and Jesus. Miss Portman, you are alive. I was so worried."

"Hey, let us out!" A fist pounded on the pantry door. Pammy, no doubt.

"Pam?" Katie headed toward the door. "What's she doing in there?"

Mr. XXX stopped Katie. "Stand aside. I'll handle this."

"Careful. There are some seriously dangerous people in there," I said, hoping somehow the door had become glued shut.

Both cops drew their guns.

"Where's the key?" The female cop looked over at Katie and then at me.

What could I do? This story had its own forward momentum and there was no choice but to go with the flow—which meant concealing the key in my pocket.

"The key? I'm, well, I don't know. In all the excitement…"

Katie and Gale searched the counter for the key.

XXX inspected the locked door and then said, "I'll be right back."

He disappeared toward the front door.

"Help," Fifi squealed from inside the pantry.

"Would someone like to explain what's going on here?" The female cop asked no one in particular.

Katie pointed to me and said, "She said there were burglars."

The cop continued her inquisition: "Who called 911?"

Merna stepped forward and said, "Miss Pam said to."

"Who's Miss Pam?" the female officer asked.

"Me," Pam shouted from inside the pantry.

Katie took a step toward the closet door. "Pam, what are you doing in there?"

Katie shot a look at me. I tried to look innocent and shrugged.

The front door slammed and XXX came striding back in with a battering ram. I'd only seen them used on that reality show, "Cops," when they stormed a suspect's home to arrest him.

He aimed the ram at the door knob and lock, then shouted in the direction of the pantry hostages, "*Stand against the back wall.*"

There was shuffling and shoving noises from the pantry.

XXX swung the battering ram back and forth a couple of times and hit the door knob dead on. The impact shook the door and XXX.

He took a step back and then swung the ram at the door again. This time wood splintered near the lock. When he hit it a third time, the door burst open.

The female officer aimed her firearm toward the gang inside the pantry.

Katie rushed forward and pulled Pam out, saying, "There's been a mistake. Pam's my assistant."

David launched out the door and into the kitchen.

"Freeze!" shouted XXX.

"Thank you, officers," David said, baffling the officers. They looked unsure about David's status.

David turned to Katie. "That's some panic room you've got there, Katie. Thanks for the tour, but you need to get your security people to work on the release mechanism."

The cops lowered the artillery.

"Excuse me?" Katie looked puzzled. "Do I know you?"

Guns raised again.

"Of course you do. Very funny. David Isaacson. Liz's agent."

Firearms lowered.

"Oh." Katie turned to me. "I thought you said they were, like, burglars."

Hell-A Rule #33: Agents can easily be mistaken for burglars, although instead of breaking into your home, they break into your peace of mind and steal your sanity.

Fifty percent of the people in the room were confused. The cops holstered their weapons.

Officer XXX asked, "So who broke into what?"

David ignored him and worked the room, extending his hand to Gale, "David Isaacson, Nevison Agency." Gale shook his hand tentatively.

"She kidnapped us. I was traumatized," Pam said as the others filed out of the pantry.

Katie gave me a puzzled look and said, "Kidnapped?"

"Now we're getting somewhere," XXX said. "Who kidnapped you?"

The cops looked at David, who slithered up to Pam, wrapping his arm around her shoulder. "Don't be hysterical, darling. It was just an accident." He crushed her to him, giving her a little shake and grinning desperately.

Pam shoved David away, almost knocking him down. "Get off me, you, you ... agent."

Pam pointed a well-manicured fingernail at me and said, "Arrest that woman, she's a psychopath."

"She's no psychopath, she's a method writer," David said as he whisked Pam toward the door to the pool area. "Liz was just working out a scene in *Jane Blonde 2*. Let's go outside and talk about your producer's fee."

"No!" Pam knocked the wind out of David with a Krav Maga elbow blow. He doubled over in embarrassment.

"Correct me if I'm wrong," Katie said. "But I think I'm totally confused."

Pam glared at me. "She held me against my will. Arrest her."

Mr. XXX stepped in. "Kidnapping is a serious offense. Twenty, 30 years in prison, unless you've had two strikes. Then it's life."

"I want to file charges." Pammy glared at me.

Officer XXX reached for his handcuffs.

Suddenly, the room shook. Everyone reached out for counters and held on.

Earthquake!

CUT TO THE PAST:

Beverly Hills.

I'd only been in LA two months when I got my initiation into the Quake Club.

It was 4:31 a.m. Monday, January 19, 1994. I thought someone had broken into my apartment and was shaking the bed. But then I heard glass breaking in the living room and things really started rocking and rolling. I realized it was my first earthquake.

The bed started heading for the south wall of the bedroom. I grabbed Aggie under one arm and leapt onto the floor, which was pitching up and down violently. I was thrown up against the chest of drawers.

Just as I made a hop toward the bathroom doorway, I felt the electric wire of my portable TV brush the back of my calf, as it did a flip and crashed into the pine floor. One second sooner and it would have broken my leg or worse.

I made it to the bathroom doorframe and wedged myself in so hard that I strained every muscle from my neck to my heels. I held Aggie tight under one arm. The pitching and rumbling and booming and swaying and cracking went on for what seemed like 30 minutes. I knew that the floor would be falling any moment. Maybe the roof, too. I prayed I wouldn't die.

Hell-A Rule #34: Never move to LA without a current last will and testament. Your life's on the line on a daily basis. If the drive-bys don't get you, the earthquakes will.

The house rocked to a stop. Then there was another boom and it started again. It stopped a second time. I heard car alarms going off all over the neighborhood. Everything else was silent.

I dashed to the phone and called my mother in Florida. It was just after 7:30 there and she was still in bed.

"Mother, there was an earthquake. I think it was a bad one. But I'm okay."

She had been asleep and mumbled, "Okay, honey." Then she hung up.

One second later, the phone lines went down. Aggie and I went outside where everyone from our building was congregated on the sidewalk. It was like some bizarre middle-of-the-night, open-air pajama party.

"Are you all right?" people kept asking each other, dazed from the shaking the planet had just given us. Strangers living 20 feet from each other now became family. We realized our electricity was still on, but everything south of us was blacked out. There was some advantage to living in Beverly Hills proper.

I went back upstairs and turned on the TV in the living room. The first news reports came in. A news crew was covering a gas main rupture on Balboa in Granada Hills a couple of blocks from where one of my writing partners lived. The street was on fire. Houses along the street were on fire. It looked biblical.

I watched until the sun came up and by then reports were coming in from all over the city. The pictures weren't pretty. The Antelope Valley Freeway had collapsed and a motorcycle cop had dropped off the edge, falling to his death. A house had pancaked on a Sherman Oaks hillside, killing the owners. The Northridge mall was in shambles. So was part of Northridge College. The Northridge Meadows apartment complex was the worst hit. The first floor was crushed by the top two floors, killing one-third of the overall 57 victims of the quake.

Soon the burst of earth energy would have a name: The Northridge Earthquake. The magnitude was disputed for days after the initial jolts. It was 6.6, or was it 6.8?

The epicenter was 12 miles northwest of my apartment, yet the shockwaves tore down the I-10 freeway a couple of miles south of me. In other words, there was enough energy running under our building to rip apart steel, cement and asphalt, yet our apartment was spared.

There were 6,000 aftershocks in the following months. After a week of unpredictable jolts and booms, I sat down on the steps to my deck and thought about moving back to Florida.

At least with hurricanes you could see them coming and get out of the way. Earthquakes and tremors were like the boogeyman, exploding into your life when you least expected it. Boo!

I was a wreck. Aggie was a wreck. Everyone in LA was a wreck.

But I hadn't gotten what I'd come for—a seriously excellent career in screenwriting. I wasn't going back home empty-handed. I knew I had to connect all those aftershocks with a positive thought, so I made one up: "Every time I feel the earth rumble, that's one less writer moving to California to compete with me."

So I stayed until I met Christopher, and then we both moved to Florida.

BACK TO THE PRESENT:

Bel Air.

The tremor stopped. A few of the handblown champagne glasses had broken in Katie's kitchen, but it was probably only a 2.8 or 3, so no big deal.

Just as everyone was regaining their equilibrium and the officer remembered he was thinking about arresting me, I flipped open the cabinet where I'd stashed my MP-9 and raised it toward the cops.

Before either officer could react, I took my sixth and seventh hostage of the day. I was really getting the hang of crime. It was like writing screenplays. The more you wrote, the easier it got.

"Hands up," I commanded. The cops gave each other a "Reno 911" we're-screwed look.

"Let's get outta here!" I yelped as I directed the weapon at Katie and Gale.

Both Katie and Gale were dumbfounded.

I felt terrible. A budding friendship was developing between the three of us one minute and the next I turned psycho on my new best friends.

But what else could I do? I was flying by the seat of my pants. Making up the script as I went along. It was real-life improvisation.

"What do you mean?" Katie glanced out at the far end of the pool where Hugh and his Unidentified Friend were spread out on chaises damaging their young epidermises with UV rays. They were oblivious to the action-adventure scene playing out in the kitchen and way too cool to overreact to a mere 3.0 earthquake.

We needed a getaway car. One that could outrun the police, the Feds, and the paparazzi.

"Where's your car?" I asked.

"Which one?" Katie replied.

"The fast one."

"Out there." Katie pointed toward a door off the kitchen.

I motioned for Katie and Gale to go in that direction.

"Don't leave. I can fix this." David inched toward my girls and me as we edged toward the door to the garage.

"Back off, snake boy."

He didn't. "But this could be your first big movie. I can launch your career. I can put you on the A-List." Like I'd never heard that before.

We were at the door. David was still coming.

"Stop, or I'll shoot," I promised.

David laughed, "That's really lame dialog. Can't you improvise something more original?"

"How about this?"

I shot him in the foot. The gun blast was so loud in the marble kitchen, everyone, including the police, flinched. Then Tiffany started laughing and kind of weeping alternately.

"You shot me in the foot, you bitch." David limped to a chair.

"No, you shot yourself in the foot, you bitch." I smiled unsympathetically.

As we backed out the door, I said, "First person through this door gets a mouth full of lead." Geez, now that was lame dialogue. Sounded like something from a Jimmy Cagney movie.

It was a really big garage. The floor was covered with wall-to-wall black rubber. Framed black and white photos of hot cars from the 50s cruising along PCH hung in a row down one wall, each lighted with a spot. Lined up perfectly in the center of the floor were eight of the hottest cars known to woman.

One of the reasons people in LA were so luxe car-obsessed was the blatant public display at valet stations of your transportation in front of dozens of important people you're desperate to impress. Either those you're with or those you recognize and wish you were with. After any awards party or dinner at an industry haunt, your ride is paraded in front of the mob waiting at the curb.

You are judged to be cool or uncool, wealthy or destitute the split second you head toward your car. If you're driving the cheap American compact, you are unworthy of future contact. If you're driving the six-figure import, you'll get a follow-up call while driving home.

Hell-A Rule #35: You are your car.

I really wanted to take the XK120 for a spin, but it only had two seats and there were three of us, so I spotted the perfect hot rod. It was a shiny red and white '57 Chevy Bel Air. I swung the driver's door open and motioned for Katie and Gale to get in.

Katie climbed in the front, Gale in the back.

"May I ask what your agenda is?" Gale asked, a little annoyed by the apparent lack of control on her part.

"Ah, well, I'm not really sure. It just seemed like a good time to leave, don't you think?"

She didn't answer me. I was glad because I was busy acquainting myself with the car, adjusting the rearview mirror, that kind of thing.

The keys were in the ignition. I fired her up and hit what I thought was the garage door opener on the visor. Nothing happened.

"That's, like, for the front gate. It's the other one." For a hostage, Katie was very helpful.

"Thanks." I jabbed the button of the other remote control on the visor. The garage door floated open quietly. It certainly didn't clatter like the garage door at our rental home in Florida that sounded like a wood chipper shredding a moped.

When the garage door opened all the way, I was happy to see nothing but landscaping and one empty cop car out front.

I revved the Chevy engine to 5000 rpms.

"Fasten your seatbelts. It's going to be a bumpy ride," I said wondering if either would notice my homage to the famous *All About Eve* line.

Gale said, "There are no seatbelts."

The Chevy lurched out of the garage like a ravenous tiger.

The car sped over the cobblestones and toward the gate just as XXX and his fellow officer stormed out the front door. They raised their pistols, but must have thought better of taking a chance of wounding one of Hollywood's leading actresses. How would that look in their file and on "Entertainment Tonight"?

I punched the front gate button. It slid open as two other officers in the street were getting a call from XXX. They drew their weapons when we roared by, making the right turn onto the street at the top of first gear.

Hasta la vista, baby.

Adrenaline was pumping. I felt like Thelma and Louise when they went off that cliff. I just prayed I didn't hit bottom.

Chapter Twelve

THE OBLIGATORY CAR CHASE

Bel Air.

Car chases were everyday occurrences in Hell-A. People slowed down, pulled over, but did not stop. The DMV's driver's test used a simulated car chase as a mandatory pass/fail element. If a driver's license applicant saw the simulator chasee approaching with a simulated cop car in pursuit and swerved to the curb, slamming on brakes, no driver's license would be issued.

As we sped down the hill from Katie's mansion toward Sunset Boulevard, in the rearview mirror I saw a police cruiser gaining. Cars decelerated to let us pass.

The streets were narrow and winding. The smallest miscalculation in trajectory would have resulted in disaster. A '66, or was it '67, Shelby Cobra backed out of a driveway ahead. I was going too fast to hit the brakes on a curve, so I zoomed around the exquisite machine. I was sorry we passed by so quickly. I would've loved to take a good look.

"This is totally cool. I've never been chased by the police before." Katie looked almost jubilant. Gale was quiet. I couldn't tell if she was pissed off or thinking about where she could get financing for *Jane Blonde.*

We were almost to Sunset when we ran up behind a gold Rolls-Royce. I honked the horn. The Rolls poked on down the winding lane at 10 miles an hour. The police cruiser was on my tail. I laid on the horn.

The Rolls driver stuck his hand out the window and shot a perfect bird. I hit the accelerator and swerved around the asshole.

Rolls Guy freaked and cut his wheel, crashing into a parked car. As we sped by, he struggled to open his door and get free of the white safety mushroom called an airbag.

The sudden evasive action threw Katie against the passenger door and sent Gale sliding off the backseat onto her ass on the floorboard. I wished I had remembered that there were no seatbelts in a '57 Chevy.

Gale scrambled back up onto the seat and snapped, "Do you have to drive so recklessly?"

I was too busy driving recklessly to answer.

I slowed down at the traffic light at Sunset and glanced in the rearview mirror to see the cop car shear off the driver's door of the Rolls. Rolls Guy jumped out and made unfriendly gestures at the police.

Traffic was heavy on Sunset as it is every afternoon. I thought about heading south, but I could see red taillights a couple blocks down and decided to brave Sunset. At least there was a center turn lane if things got too slow.

We took a sharp turn onto Sunset, swerving around a Hollywood Star Tours bus. It was the same tour Christopher and I took my mother and Uncle Richard on when they visited.

CUT TO THE PAST:

Beverly Hills.

I lived in LA for almost seven years without buying a star map or taking a tour, but when family came to Tinseltown, they wanted to see stars, or at least the 10-foot walls around their mansions.

Fortunately, we got to see at least one "star" on our two-hour bus trip through Beverly Hills. As we approached Engelbert Humperdinck's home, a black limo backed out of the driveway, and the gates swung closed. The back window lowered and the Hump himself stuck his head out the window, waving and smiling. Older women like my mom who knew who he was swooned and squealed. Others wondered what the excitement was about.

Back home, my mom got a lot of points at her ladies' church group for seeing a big star like Hump.

BACK TO THE PRESENT:

Bel Air.

As we passed the Hollywood Star Tours bus I caught a quick glimpse of star-struck tourists getting a quick glimpse of Katie Portman. She smiled and waved to them. Cameras appeared at every window as the bus people captured the celebrity sighting on flash cards and mini-DV tape.

Weaving through traffic was like doing a fast autocross slalom, but with cars instead of pylons. The girls hung on as the Bel Air zigzagged from one lane to another.

Katie was digging it. "Wow, you're pretty good. Ever thought of stunt driving?"

"Too dangerous," I said. Katie laughed. Gale didn't.

Ahead I saw a red light and three lanes of waiting cars. I zipped into the turn lane in the center of the six-lane road. As we approached I saw very little traffic in the intersection and decided I could probably bully my way through against the light.

But as we were within three car lengths of the light, I saw a blonde in one of last year's Liz Claiborne jogging suits, striding across the road. I slammed on brakes. The Chevy fishtailed a little, but rocked to a stop just as the woman emerged from behind the waiting cars. What I couldn't see until then, was a cute little terrier and a white standard poodle prancing along in front of her on gold and leather leashes.

Oh, my, God, I would have killed myself if I had run over defenseless dogs.

The woman strolled across the pavement to the curb as if she was oblivious to her near death. Then I saw she had an iPod strapped to her arm. She was in iTunesLand without a care in this world.

At a distance, the woman's dogs reminded me so much of my little Aggie and her poodle-mix friend Sandy.

CUT TO THE PAST:

Beverly Hills.

Sandy's daddy, Tom Terrific, was one of the first people I met in LA. He was a friend of my best friends in Florida. Tom was directing TV and writing film scripts. We became friends and exchanged petsitting responsibilities.

Sandy came to stay with Aggie and me when Tom went off to direct something. Aggie stayed with Tom when I went home to visit my family in Florida.

In Beverly Hills dogs had to be on leashes. Dogs had to have city licenses. Doggie doo-doo had to be picked up with an official Tiffany's pooper-scooper. Only thoroughbred dogs that have won Best In Show at Westminster could live in Beverly Hills. Mixed breed visitors were tolerated but not encouraged. Fortunately Aggie was a Norfolk terrier. Her father was Paprika of White Hall, a Westminster champion, but that didn't matter to me or Aggie, who never knew her champion father. We weren't going to be trotting around any dog show ring any time soon.

Since Norfolks were rare on the West Coast, Aggie got a lot of attention on the street. And since Aggie was a yapper, our walks of biological necessity stressed me out. On our beach in Florida we would see one, maybe two dogs during our 20-minute walks. On Oakhurst Drive in Beverly Hills, we would see at least 20 dogs on our two-minute walks. And every dog or even anything that moved warranted a barking fit from the Agster.

For some reason, when Sandy came to visit, Aggie was on her best behavior. When I took them both for walks, Aggie became the world's friendliest dog. Maybe it was because Sandy was so mellow and Aggie didn't want to make a fool of herself.

During one visit Sandy disappeared. She and Aggie had been sunning on the deck with Sandy wearing one of Aggie's sweaters to ward off the spring chill. I discovered Sandy missing and the back gate to the alley open.

I freaked and ran into the alley screaming Sandy's name, which didn't help matters since Sandy was totally deaf. She was nowhere to be seen. I raced to the front of the building, down the street pleading with everyone I met, "Have you seen a big white dog in a little red sweater?"

I dashed down to Olympic, dreading that I would see a red and white lump in the middle of the six-lane speedway. Since Sandy was deaf and wasn't accustomed to fending for herself in LA rush-hour traffic, I expected the worst. No Sandy.

I darted up and down the street in sheer panic. Where was my diazepam when I needed it?

Hell-A Rule #36: All residents of LA County are required to have a current prescription for valium or other pharmaceutically equivalent tranquilizer. Life in the City of Angels without modern medicine is impossible.

I ran into my Lebanese neighbors in front of our building.

"Where is your angry dog?" the father asked.

Since Aggie barked incessantly at everything that moved outside, my neighbors called her The Angry Dog.

"She's upstairs, but I've lost the white dog," I said, near tears.

"Oh, the nice dog who do not bark."

"She's deaf and dumb." I could tell they didn't understand the dumb part. What did a dog's IQ have to do with anything?

"Oh, the white dog, she in the alley beside…"

I was in the alley before he finished the sentence.

"Sandy! Sandy!" Calling for her when I knew she couldn't hear anything just went to prove I was the dumb one.

Then I saw a flash of red and white down the alley. Sandy wandered out from behind a giant garbage can. I ran to her, so relieved to have found her alive and well. Sandy and Aggie spent the rest of the week hanging out on the deck, going for walks in Roxbury Park, eating and sleeping, dreaming doggie dreams.

I never told Tom about Sandy's adventure. It would be the last time Sandy visited us. Less than two months later, Sandy died peacefully in her sleep at Tom's apartment.

Tom was heartbroken and couldn't face looking for another canine friend. He threw himself into his work. He went on to be senior producer of "Survivor" starting with the first season and later became "Survivor's" Executive Producer. He also got married, started a family and adopted a new dog.

BACK TO THE PRESENT:

Bel Air.

Police sirens closed in.

In the rearview mirror, I saw the police cruiser that followed us from our swerve onto Sunset. Drivers around us saw the flashing lights, heard the screaming sirens and tried to pull over. It was vehicular chaos. A second police cruiser joined the medium-speed chase. Probably Officer XXX.

Then, behind us I saw the most awesome sight: an armada of helicopters flying straight down Sunset behind us. Then I noticed flashing red and blue lights on top of black and white cars gaining on us in the center lane. Jesus Christ Superstar, it looked like a John Woo movie.

At that moment I was feeling the need for speed.

Obviously the Beverly Hills and Los Angeles Police Departments connected the Nevison invasion and hostage-taking with the Katie Portman kidnapping and called in reinforcements. You can bet David and the others had spilled their guts about their harrowing journey to Ms. Portman's estate, especially since I cut them out of the deal and made David bleed. A mad agent is a bad agent.

Katie glanced back to see the entourage. She clapped her hands. "This is so adrenalicious," she shouted over the approaching rumble of the news and police helicopters.

"It's not a movie, Katie. It's real life." Gale was a great producer. One thing that made a good producer great was having a stranglehold on reality and Gale had tackled reality and wrestled it to the ground a long time ago.

"That's what makes it, like, so exciting."

I swerved around a Mini Cooper stretch limo and hauled ass down the center lane. A Lamborghini waiting to make a turn saw us coming dead ahead and darted into traffic to avoid us. Over the annoying whine of sirens, I heard the shriek of car horns, screeching of tires and crashing noises behind us. I was acutely aware the chopper-cams above must be getting it all on high-def.

In the side mirror, I saw mangled metal and steam rising from punctured radiators. It was a sobering reminder that someone could get hurt. Katie glanced back at Gale, less excited now as the possibility of ending up being rescued by the jaws-of-life set in.

Westwood.

We wove in and out of traffic until Sunset became a parking lot. Nothing but a snake of red taillights ahead. Stalled traffic in the oncoming lanes. It was always like this in the afternoons in Westwood as commuters headed home or students hurried to classes at UCLA.

I spotted an escape route: the turn signal at UCLA's north entrance. As it was changing to yellow, I scooched in behind a VW and drifted the 90-degree turn at 45 miles per hour. A controlled slide is a beautiful thing to witness and an even more beautiful thing to execute.

I always got a rush walking through the UCLA campus. It was the stately brick buildings with their wide, welcoming stairs. It was the history of those who had studied film here before me. It was the bustle of starry-eyed students. You never knew if the kid sitting next to you in class would turn out to be the year's hottest new director or a famous serial killer.

One of the advantages for a screenwriter living in LA is taking classes through UCLA's Writers Extension Program. I took at least one course every semester until I had gone through the entire catalog for film writers.

Driving onto campus now in a cherry '57 Chevy with Katie Portman and Gale Grazer, I felt as if I had transcended. I hoped someone I knew would see us. Of course, with the entire police force of Beverly Hills and their friends from LA along with our eight-chopper escort, everyone would see us.

As we wound through the narrow streets of the campus at 5 miles per hour with our noisy escort, every pedestrian stopped to stare. Among them was a teacher who had become a friend, the writer who had advised me against wasting time on an original pitch for Bali, my friend who was ghostwriting Asian action-adventure movies, my friend who was flabbergasted to see me driving a vintage muscle car filled with Hollywood elite.

I tooted the horn and waved. He raised his hand as if he were going to wave, but his hand hung there in thin air just like his jaw.

Since I was distracted, I missed the fork in the road that went south on the campus and ended up approaching a student parking structure.

Parking garages creeped me out. Somehow when I took the ticket and I cruised into a parking garage, it was like driving into Supernatural Territory. Strange things happened.

CUT TO THE PAST:

Century City.

The first time I parked in the Century Plaza Hotel garage, I was perfectly on time to pick up my writing partner, Bill Kelley, for studio meetings until I discovered that valet parking at the front door of the hotel was $18. I checked my wallet. Five lousy one-dollar bills.

> *Hell-A Rule #37: All drivers must keep a large cash reserve on hand for valet parking, which can range from $4 to $40. Street parking is rarely available. Besides, anyone actually walking on the sidewalk for more than a block will be arrested for vagrancy.*

I sped away as the valet captain tried to open my car door. I found the Century Plaza's self-parking garage, but had to drive up seven floors before I located a parking space.

Then I lost the ticket I needed for free parking validation. I searched the car. Nothing but old Coffee Bean receipts and penis enhancement discount coupons.

I was shouting profanity at myself when I saw a security guard. I dashed toward him. He took a step back, his hand going to his nightstick.

"I can't find my ticket."

He eyed me and said, "Twenty-five dollars for lost tickets."

"Twenty-five?! I could have valeted for 18." I was flinging my hands about like a demented cartoon character. "I'm going to kill myself."

"You could see the concierge in the hotel. Maybe they can help you," he said as he hurried away.

When I got to the ground floor, I realized I was 15 minutes late. I hated being late. I looked around to see I was in a service area, sort of an outdoor basement, and I couldn't get to the hotel entrance from there. I howled and stamped my foot.

It was hot for California and makeup was running down my neck and into my new Bloomingdale's sale blouse. My head was about to explode.

I sprinted to the ticket booth cashier and screamed, "How do I get to the damn hotel?"

He looked alarmed and quickly pointed to the elevator. "Bridge on the second floor."

When I arrived at the restaurant 23 minutes late, Bill was already on his second hand-squeezed orange juice and vodka. He believed in getting well fortified before taking on the horrors of Hollywood.

"I was just sending out Search and Rescue, kiddo." Bill stood up and gave me a bear hug. I was sweaty, flushed, and lovable.

We didn't talk about our day's meetings over breakfast. It was bad luck, Bill said. Over-preparing for a pitch or meeting was a bit like an actor over-rehearsing. We didn't want the performance to come off as wooden and not spontaneous.

Because LA traffic was predictable, I knew to leave an hour before our first meeting, only 15 minutes away.

We were almost to the hotel lobby exit, when I remembered my lost ticket crisis and stopped by the concierge's desk while Bill waited near the door. I explained my dilemma.

The concierge smiled and said, "Oh, I'm so sorry. Lost tickets are $25."

I looked over at Bill, who was wondering what the hell I was doing.

"See that man? He's Bill Kelley, a very famous writer. He won an Academy Award for *Witness* with Harrison Ford and we're going to see Harrison right now about a new movie we're writing for him." Well, the first part of the sentence was true.

"I loved *Witness*. Harrison Ford, isn't that wonderful?"

The concierge quickly handed me a get-out-of-the-garage-free pass and beamed. "Have a great day. Say hello to Mr. Ford for me."

Bill waited at the grand front entrance while I retrieved the car. Only thing was, in the madness that followed my entry into the garage, I couldn't remember where I parked. Parking amnesia courtesy of the Outer Limits.

I ran wildly through the garage, up ramps, down ramps. The same security guard who had witnessed my meltdown earlier was now cruising the place in an electric cart.

"I can't find my car," I shouted out at him. He saw me and burned rubber in the opposite direction. I finally found my car after 15 minutes of panic.

When I picked Bill up at the Century Plaza entrance, he said, "For a former race car driver, you're awfully slow."

BACK TO THE PRESENT:

Westwood.

I stopped 30 feet from the UCLA parking garage entrance. Thinking ahead, I reasoned if I led the chase into the six-story garage, the '57 Chevy would end up leaping off the sixth floor, hoping to safely land on a bridge close by, or at least that's what would happen in a Jane Blonde script. But since there was no bridge on campus, and this wasn't a stunt scene, I figured avoiding being trapped was a good plan.

I revved the engine and did a second-gear autocross start, wrestling the wheel to make a 90-degree turn. The big Chevy wheels rolled up onto the curb, onto a median, over rows of impatiens and boxwoods, onto the road I had intended on taking in the first place.

My teacher friend who had distracted me into taking the wrong turn to the parking garage, stood on the sidewalk, hardly believing his eyes as I piloted the police cruisers on a surreal parade through campus.

We came to a bottleneck where two lanes of traffic were stopped at a red light headed off campus. Some cars tried to pull over when they saw the police. I jammed the gearbox into first and took off around the line into a lane of incoming traffic. Cars swerved, blowing their horns, crashing into planters and veering onto the sidewalk.

The Chevy bottomed out as we made a right-hand turn from the campus onto Hilgard. A loud scraping noise came from the undercarriage of the car.

"Sorry." I hated wrecking a cherry classic like this baby.

Katie was almost cheerful. "It's okay. I was thinking of getting rid of some of the cars anyway. It's really obsessive, having so many."

It was hard to hear over the chopper roar. "What?"

"The car's not important. Really."

Gale leaned into the conversation and yelled, "It's an investment!" She was obviously a collector. "With the right vintage portfolio, you're set for life."

Katie laughed, "It's just money."

Gale couldn't think of a response. Most people in her tax bracket couldn't.

There was a break in oncoming traffic and I made a quick left turn into a quiet residential neighborhood. Our colorful entourage followed.

In the middle of the block ahead, I spotted a parking enforcement officer and her little three-wheeled electric car. She was awarding tickets to cars illegally parked in the PERMIT PARKING ONLY zone. I sympathized with residents living around UCLA since if left unregulated, students would occupy 100 percent of all on-street parking.

CUT TO THE PAST:

West Hollywood.

In LA, there were parking traps. The city of West Hollywood was one big parking trap, which I learned upon my first visit to the Bodhi Tree, bookstore of enlightenment.

I had been enlightened to the tune of $78.59: $43.59 for the books and $35 for the parking ticket. When I got back to my car and found the citation, I looked for signs or an expired parking meter. Seeing none, I thought the ticket must be a mistake. I went back to Bodhi Tree to ask if they'd had other customers who'd been visited by the parking Nazis.

The young woman who looked as if she needed to read some of the books on de-stressing went on a tirade about the totalitarian government entrapping gentle souls in their parking scam. But how was anyone supposed to know it's permit parking only if there were no signs?

"There are signs. But they're 12 feet in the air, tiny and only posted at the end of each block. Klingon bastards."

Star Trek alien baddies flashed across the silver screen of my memory. Klingons would now and forever more be linked with LA parking enforcement officers and their little three-wheeled, battle-ready scooters.

"I hate those spiteful little people and their damned ego-trips."

I left before Miss Bodhi Tree screwed up her karma.

Sure enough, outside 12 feet in the air, on a sign about 12 inches square planted in cement near the corner was: WARNING -- PERMIT PARKING ONLY. Blah. Blah. Blah.

I paid the $35 and never parked in West Hollywood again.

> *Hell-A Rule #38: If by some supernatural event you find metered parking on the street, never leave your car unless you're absolutely, positively certain you understand the arcane regulations about allowed parking times on the sign. If you see no parking signs, run for your life, you've just entered the Twilight Parking Zone.*

BACK TO THE PRESENT:

Westwood.

The meter maid in the middle of the road ahead looked up from her current citation to see our police chase heading her way. She dove in between cars onto the sidewalk.

As we blasted past the three-wheeler, I misjudged the distance between the Chevy and the meter maid's electric car. The sideview mirror on the passenger's side clipped the back of the parking enforcement vehicle and blew up. Some chrome on it smashed into the closed window where Katie was sitting. It happened so fast, Katie didn't react until we were almost to the end of the street.

"Wow. Did you see that?"

She eyed the place where the sideview mirror had been. Shreds of metal pieces hung off the spot like something from *Terminator*.

One minute it was there, the next minute it was in tiny pieces all over the neighborhood.

I glanced back at Gale. She was gripping the top of the front seats so hard, her fingernails were digging into the upholstery.

"Watch the leather. It looks original," I suggested helpfully.

She didn't hear me. Or maybe she was ignoring me.

I came to an intersection, did a California stop at the stop sign, tapping the brake a beat, and then made a quick turn. A gleaming silver DeLorean limo was pulling out of the circular drive of a hotel. As I slowed, I realized the hotel was the first place I'd ever spent the night in LA.

CUT TO THE PAST:

Westwood.

It was a hotel where everyone knew my name. Not because I was a famous screenwriter, but because I was wearing a nametag like all the other attendees of the screenwriters conference I flew in for.

It was my first visit to California and I was in a fit of optimistic delirium for the four days of the conference. Endorphins pumped through my circulatory system giving me a nonstop barbiturate-like high. I guess the jet lag also had something to do with my spacey condition and I'm sure it was directly responsible for the attack of amnesia I had the day after I arrived.

Right after lunch I was seized with an urge for horizontal meditation, or nap as we call it in the South. There was no time for a Sunday-afternoon-on-the-couch kind of respite, but 30 minutes was better than nothing. I went up to my room and set the alarm to ensure I didn't accidentally fall into REM sleep.

Thirty minutes later I was transported into my own thriller story. The alarm went off. I bolted straight up in bed, just like in the horror films. But there was no monster, no stalker, no memory.

I couldn't figure out who I was or what I was doing in this luxurious room. My brain couldn't even put together what the alarm clock noise was. I couldn't read. My memory was completely AWOL. So I whacked the source of the audio irritation until the alarm stopped.

Quietly I sat at the edge of the bed. A remarkable peacefulness surrounded me. When you have a super-sized case of amnesia, you have no stress, no anxiety, no identity.

I'd gone from wannabe Hollywood screenwriter with an endorphin rush to Buddha.

There was a booklet on the nightstand: HOLLYWOOD SCREENWRITERS FORUM. There were symbols and letters written on the cover, but since I couldn't read, I had no idea what any of it meant.

As I stared at: PRIVATE CONSULTATION and AGENT, a wave of anxiety hit me. The words seemed familiar, although I couldn't comprehend them. Whatever they meant made me feel like I'd eaten too much cotton candy at the fair.

I held the handwritten list up to the clock. Then a tiny flash of life as it had been before the nap assaulted my brain. Time. The box with the symbols and the symbols on the list were something to do with time. Something important.

Grabbing the notepad and booklet, I took off out the door. In the hallway everything looked the same. I wasn't even sure which door I had come out of. I wandered around until I found something that looked different. Double steel doors.

Suddenly there was a loud ding. One of the sets of shiny doors swooshed open. A young man rushed off.

The young man said, "Liz, there you are. I thought you had a consultation."

I just smiled as he dashed down the hall. I was happy to know my name. I assumed that since he knew me and he had come out of the little room with the mirrors, I should go in. Once I got inside, I didn't know what to do. The doors closed and the little room started going down. Then a bell rang again and the doors slid open.

A size 18 woman charged into the little room, pushing me out as she said, "Hi, Liz. Don't you have a consultation with that agent now? You shouldn't be late."

I stepped into a big room with marble floors. I checked the booklet. PRIVATE CONSULTATION, AGENT. Where the hell was that?

I saw a long counter with people dressed alike. I showed one of them my booklet. She pointed toward a hall. I kept showing people the booklet until I got to a desk where a frantic young woman looked up and said, "Liz, you're late. He's waiting."

"Sorry." Words were coming back to me.

She ushered me into a room containing chairs, tables and people. There was one empty chair. Mine.

I was so relieved to have that puzzle solved that I just plopped down, then realized I had zero idea what I was doing there. None.

The man across the table said, "So what do you need to know?"

I couldn't think of a thing.

"Everything," I said.

This person called AGENT launched into a lecture about Hollywood. As he spoke, my memory seeped back into my conscious mind. I started taking notes, which pleased AGENT.

I suddenly remembered what AGENT was and knew that I was face to face with the most important element of my new screenwriting career. Just as the monitor was bringing in another lamb to the slaughter, I blurted out, "Do you want to read my screenplay?"

"Sure. Send it to my assistant. Next."

Of course, I know now, you never, ever, upon risk of death, ask anyone in Hollywood if they want to read your screenplay. You must wait for them to hear about your luscious new story from someone else they envy and hate, then they'll call you or your agent and beg. That's exactly what you want: begging.

At the end of the conference I knew I had to move to Los Angeles to launch a full-out assault on the fortress known as Hollywood. Two months later, I did.

BACK TO THE PRESENT:

Westwood.

The silver limo slowly eased down the street so as we cruised by, I took a long look at the sacred place where my screenwriting career began. I could have never   believed all those years ago, that someday I would be driving by the hotel with a world- famous actress and her producer. I would have never thought all those years ago that I would have been capable of kidnapping that famous actress and her producer. But once you're a slave to Hollywood, reality bends in unexpected ways and anything is possible. Just like in the movies.

I took a couple of right-hand turns and ended up on Westwood again.

When we got down to Wilshire, a wall of traffic blocked the intersection even though we had a green light. It happened all the time. People in a panic to get home or to yoga class or to acting class or to traffic school can't stand for one more driver to get in front of them.

Behind us, the queue of police cars stopped, trapping us. The swarm of choppers hovered overhead. The cops behind us jumped out of their car with their weapons in serious business position. Other officers behind them did the same.

My heart pounded. This was it. I would go to jail for the rest of my life. At least I wouldn't have to worry about paying the rent while I was finishing another spec.

I was thinking about calling Zen Man to rescue me when a distorted voice from a loudspeaker said something we couldn't hear over the rotor roar of the helicopters above. I worried that it was something important. Maybe they were trying to tell us to do a specific thing and if we didn't do whatever it was they would open fire. The death scene in *Bonnie and Clyde* flashed into my consciousness.

Katie looked at me like I was the director and shouted, "What now?"

"You're trapped. Give up. Be realistic." Gale released her grip on the upholstery, rolled her window down and stuck her hands out.

I'd never thought of myself as realistic. I had always strived for supernatural.

The loudspeaker blasted a command that sounded like, "Step out of the *char*." Step out of the char. Not a positive image.

I was once again caught by the red light at the confluence of thought and action.

I had to think fast. Go with the flow and be slammed to the ground in two minutes.

Or do what I always did when I got hemmed in: make a U-turn.

Chapter Thirteen

CREATING HEAT

Westwood.

I revved the engine, turned the wheel as hard as I could, popped the clutch and did a perfect U-turn autocross start. The rear wheels smoked as the back end of the car swung around. I love when that happens.

Instantly, we were headed in the opposite direction.

But the road was solid police cars, curb to curb. There were curious on-lookers gathered on the sidewalks. I was at a dead end. But in the movies there was always a secret door, one that the camera didn't reveal until the hero dove through it to live another day. I had to find that door.

The police barricade looked immovable. The pedestrians did not. I knew from past experience that when faced with 3,000 pounds of metal hurling toward them, spectators could be amazingly agile.

CUT TO THE PAST:

Key West.

Autocrossing is one of the few auto sports accessible to amateurs. You can race your SUV or your stock Caddy if you want. You'll get something smaller and lower to the ground if you decide to be competitive.

Since autocross is primarily designed to see how fast you can maneuver your vehicle through a specially designed race course delineated by pylons, speed is not the only factor. Points are deducted for any pylons knocked over or missed. And you're out of the running if you forget where the next station is and go off course.

My boyfriend owned a tricked-out Scirocco and he's the one who got me into SCCA (Sports Car Club of America). He said I was a natural, having grown up in the infield of the Daytona Beach International Speedway. I raced the Scirocco and competed with the boys, winning many of my races. I could even get that VW up on three wheels in a 360-degree loop. But I wanted faster. We installed a rollbar in the Jensen Healey I owned and I ran it in a few races. It looked fast. Bright yellow convertibles always look fast. But I wanted to race with the really big boys. I wanted to race formula. They're not street legal. They're too low, too fast and too dangerous. I had to have one.

About the time my obsession came to a peak, a Formula Vee came on the market. I bought it. Then I discovered why there were no women driving formula cars in South Florida. The steering wheel ratio compared with the patch on the track required upper body strength most women didn't have. The patch is the rubber that comes in contact with the asphalt and changes as the car moves through the course.

So I started pumping iron and got as buff as I could get without abusing steroids. It was enough to control the car on the course, but not enough for me to win. The faster I went, the more brute strength I needed to hold the car on the course.

Which leads me back to my experience with pedestrians dodging speeding cars—I almost ran down a crowd at the Conch Republic Days parade.

It was a stupid idea to begin with. Members of our sports car club drove their cars in the parade, revving the engines to give the folks a thrill. Actually, that wasn't the stupid part. Lame, but not stupid.

Here's the stupid part. Our cars were led by a pickup truck full of pylons. Someone jumped off the back of the truck with cones and set up a slalom course in the middle of the public street lined with hundreds of innocent, trusting spectators. The five of us driving would show off our expert driving skills weaving in and out of the pylons. Then there was a truck behind picking up the pylons.

If we had only stayed focused on the point of the exhibition, giving the good citizens of Key West a little thrill, everything would've been fine. But, no. What happens when you put five racers on asphalt with pylons? They get competitive. We got faster and faster. More and more daring. Swerving and screeching. The crowd was wowed until my accelerator stuck. Then I was the one who was wowed.

The throttle jammed wide open and I couldn't control the car. There was a split second of panic as my Formula Vee veered off course, headed straight for the curb where children and their parents applauded. I mean *I* panicked, not the spectators. They probably thought it was part of the show. I was inches away from vehicular homicide when I stood on the brakes, slammed the gear-shift to neutral and put every ounce of adrenaline I had pumping through my biceps into turning that fiberglass missile away from those human targets.

People leapt back instinctively. The engine roared as it guzzled Cam Fuel unrestrained. The front right tire grazed the curb as I fought to turn the car back into the street. Pedestrians ran.

Then the engine stalled and the car jerked to a stop in the middle of the street. The parade behind me came to a halt. Only one driver following me had seen the incident. The others slalomed on down the street unaware of the mayhem that had almost occurred.

I snapped open the five-point harness and leapt out of the car, adrenaline flooding my bloodstream.

The driver behind me stopped to help me push the car off the road. "What the hell just happened?"

"Throttle cable." I took my helmet off and looked over at the family on the sidewalk I almost murdered. "No big deal."

I had learned denial early in life. It served me well in many mind-crushing instances. This had been one.

BACK TO THE PRESENT:

Westwood.

I swerved onto a parking garage ramp, made a left turn onto the sidewalk and blasted past the roadblock. Pedestrians dove for safety as we sped to the corner, down the handicap curb and out onto the asphalt again. I heard someone let out a whoop. It was me.

The policemen holstered their guns and leapt back into their cruisers, all making U-turns in the middle of Westwood Boulevard in a Chinese fire drill maneuver. Choppers darted around each other to follow the action like dragonflies in a feeding frenzy.

By this time, text messaging and cell calls had alerted students about the human drama unfolding in their neighborhood. Hundreds of cheering fans lined the street. This all looked familiar. Then it occurred to me that this was one block away from where O.J. had come off the 405, headed to his Rockingham estate at the end of his history-making slow-speed chase. Dozens of people were standing in the street cheering him on.

CUT TO THE PAST:

Beverly Hills.

I had watched the standoff on television with all of America. I watched the arrest, the cartoonish, sitcom-without-a-laugh-track murder trial on Court TV and the verdict being read. I was shocked and dismayed at the not guilty verdict. There was a trail of blood from the murder scene to O.J.'s house. There was DNA and the infamous glove. There was incriminating evidence galore.

How could any jury not see the man was guilty? After I thought about it, I realized that this was Hollywood, and a Hollywood ending could be tacked onto any story, even if it didn't fit. The trial was a show put on for the judge, jury and the American public. O.J. Simpson didn't go free because he was not guilty, he went free because his clever attorneys created a compelling passion play about corrupt, racist cops framing an innocent black American sports hero and the jury bought it.

The day after the verdict was read, a friend who lived a couple doors east of the crime scene called me to say that someone had taped laser-printed flyers on lamp posts on San Vicente Boulevard in Brentwood saying: WARNING: MURDERER ON THE LOOSE.

BACK TO THE PRESENT:

Westwood.

But I wasn't a murderer, I was just an innocent screenwriter righting a wrong. The jury would sympathize. After all, any jury assembled in metro LA would be made up of frustrated screenwriters, aspiring screenwriters, or valets who were sure they were writing the next blockbuster. They would all understand my motivation.

I thought of giving up. Of just stopping the car, getting out, lying down and letting them cuff me. But one of the things my dad taught me was never give up. That's how I got in this mess to begin with.

So, I drove on. The campus was coming up again, so I turned onto a street I knew led back down to Wilshire.

Gale leaned forward and yelled. "Where the hell are you going?"

"Ah…I…don't know. Any suggestions?"

I was coming up on a Wilshire Boulevard intersection again. Fortunately the light was green and, oddly enough, the traffic was not gridlocked.

"How about the beach? The sun should be setting soon and that would, like, make awesome footage on the news. All those cop cars with flashing lights…" Katie gesticulated exuberantly as she visualized the scene. "And police with their pistols drawn and all of us, the victims of…of circumstances." Katie should be a director.

"Okey dokey."

West LA.

On the way down to Olympic Boulevard, we passed a fleet of shiny new limos. When you saw a limo, you never knew if it was George Clooney or just some Beverly Hills High kids going out for a burger. All the windows were blacked out. Getting used to seeing limos cruising the streets was one of my first challenges as a new resident of LA. You learned not to stare or even look at them directly. Cool meant not noticing when you saw a stretch limo the length of a Mardi Gras float.

Celebrities tried to outdo each other with their limos, adapting anything into a custom luxury party-mobile. Hummer limos, Mini limos, monster truck limos, PT Cruiser limos, Geo Metro limos. It was like rednecks and their trucks: The more crap you could put on the thing, the cooler it was. Or at least that was the objective, to make people look and feel special.

CUT TO THE PAST:

Beverly Hills.

My first Oscar Week was bizarro. Famous stars, directors and producers descended upon our little town like locusts on corn, or potatoes, or whatever it is that they devour. You couldn't go out to dinner without being forced to dine with Emma Thompson, Quentin Tarantino or Spike Lee. Adoring fans gathered across from popular celeb haunts like The Four Seasons, Beverly Hills Hotel, the Peninsula, and the Beverly Wilshire to scream and take photos when their favorite star emerged to dive into his limo.

I spent Oscar Night at Women in Film's Academy Awards viewing party at The House of Blues. Leaving about 11:00 in a stream of industry folks headed to other parties, I had a relatively quick run from Sunset to Melrose. But then I came upon an amazing sight: bumper-to-bumper limos as far as I could see.

One of the biggest parties every Oscar Night is held at Morton's. It's the Vanity Fair party and all the award winners are there. Little did I know I had merged into the wrong lane and somehow was trapped in the never-ending parade of limos circling the blocks around Morton's. So there I was in my old silver Saab in a sluggish river of shiny new black and white stretch limos, going round and round.

I did get to see Whoopi Goldberg waving to crazed fans as she went into Morton's. The throng cordoned off across the street from Morton's and screamed out stars' names as they popped out of their limos. It was near hysteria as I slowly cruised by in the crush of luxury autos.

After circling the event four times in the stream of limos, I finally nosed my way into the escape lane, ran a red light, and fled south until I hit stalled traffic near The Four Seasons.

I finally caught on to the limo logic and realized there was nowhere for hundreds of limos to park, so the drivers had to keep on driving. That made every street in Beverly Hills a slow-moving parking lot. Instead of going ballistic as I usually did in gridlock, I decided to enjoy the Oscar Night cruising.

I let myself get caught in all the important traffic jams. I did the Vanity Fair traffic jam again, then took a detour to Chasen's, where one of the big hoodoos was hoodooing. I may not have gone to the Oscars or gotten into any of the big parties, but I was rubbing bumpers with Tom Hanks and Carrot Top. At least that should count for something.

BACK TO THE PRESENT:

West LA.

Our escort of cop cruisers and helicopters fell a block or so behind. Were they backing off because we were headed for a trap? I strained to see as far as I could down the street and detected nothing unusual. Maybe they were going to throw spike strips across the road or maybe they backed off because we were going too fast for the neighborhood.

> *Hell-A Rule #39: Certain neighborhoods have designated chase speed limits. Anytime the chasee exceeds that boundary, the cops back off to allow the chase to cool down. Also LAPD only sends their most photogenic officers on chases. That way when they apprehend the subject, they look terrific on camera when they beat the hell out of the criminal.*

Since there are 10.5 car chases per day in LA County, the police are experts at reasonably safe pursuit. I knew we were in good hands with these guys. I certainly wouldn't have tried this stunt in Baker County where my mom lives out in the Northeast Florida woods. The sheriff and his boys would run us off the road into the swamp and shoot our asses.

We blew by the convoy of limos and got down to Olympic. I was grateful to slow things down. We could see the crowds cheering along the road better. I made a right turn onto Olympic headed toward the beach.

With the irritation of rotor noise and sirens further away, we could again hear ourselves rave on, like characters in an animated sci-fi, action-adventure comedy.

My cell phone rang. I thought I had turned it off. Huh. I checked the number, in case it was the police. I'd seen the movies. They would have a hostage negotiator try to make me think he was my best friend and persuade me to give up. Screw that.

But the number on the cell phone screen was one near and dear to my heart— Christopher's. An impulse told me to answer. It may be the last time I talked to my beloved. I flipped the phone open and put it to my ear.

"I'm sorry," I said.

There was a moment of dead air before Christopher's Kiwi accent came through loud and clear, "Tell me you are not leading a police chase down Olympic Boulevard…"

"*Look out!*" Katie screamed.

Ahead were three lanes of cars backed up at a signal light. I veered into the middle turn lane and passed the waiting motorists. As I swerved, I dropped the cell phone. As we went under the 405 overpass there was a three-lane safety gap in traffic.

Hell-A Rule #40: Never stop your vehicle under an overpass or bridge after an earthquake. If you're unlucky enough to be trapped

*in traffic during an aftershock and 50 tons of steel and concrete
overhead have a catastrophic failure, so will you.*

Just as we approached the intersection, the signal light changed to green. Since there was no camera light to capture violations, opposing traffic darted through against the light. I narrowly missed a VW and clipped the right rear bumper of a billboard truck.

LA is the only place with so much traffic that a truck towing a trailer carrying two back-to-back billboards advertising new movie releases made sense. The billboard truck jackknifed and took out a lamppost and parked cars in a lot on the corner.

Katie screamed again as another red light violator just missed the back of the Chevy. We made it through the intersection unscathed except for our psyches.

I searched for my cell phone and Christopher's soothing voice, but it was nowhere to be found. After two near collisions, I gave up on finding it until after we were arrested.

I glanced back at the flock of news choppers following and said, "I can't wait to see this video on the internet."

Katie looked over into the back seat at a iPad 2 on the floorboard. "We can watch it live."

Gale followed her gaze. "You're kidding me, right?" Gale picked up the iPad and handed it to Katie. She clicked it on and found live feed right away.

"Look, look, it's us! Awesome!" Katie showed me the screen. It looked like any other live pursuit, 'cept the dangerous criminal seen through the driver's window looked an awful lot like my mother's oldest daughter.

She clicked the volume to full-tilt boogie. "...headed west on Olympic.

Witnesses report that at least one bankable actress is a passenger in the beautifully restored, ah…looks like a '57 Chevy."

"Can't they say our names?" Katie pulled a cell phone from her pocket. "I'm calling them." She started punching buttons.

I saw no reason to try to confiscate her phone. After all, every cop in LA knew where we were and what was happening.

I looked over at her. "No. I mean, is that a good idea?"

"Of course it is. You can't buy this kind of publicity."

Gale leaned in. "She's right. Maybe we can end this right now before anyone gets hurt. Tell your story to one of the anchors. The police will see it, realize you're not a real criminal, then everything will be over."

"But I shot my agent."

"Every writer does that sometime during their career. The judge will be lenient." Gale made a good argument. And God knows I would like to get out of this alive. I had more stories to write before I permanently became one with the Spirit in the Sky again.

"Okay, call them."

Katie dialed a cell concierge. "Hi, can you connect me with KCAL? This is Katie Portman."

Some drivers on Olympic merged right when they saw us coming with our flashy escort. Others just proceeded in their usual competitive rush-hour panic, daring us to pass. We took the center lane, carefully swerving into oncoming traffic when necessary and dodging insults from the inconvenienced hordes.

Katie chatted with the anchors at KCAL News. As she told our story, it was being broadcast live on TV and the internet.

Katie tried to hand me the phone, "They want to talk to you."

I accelerated through an intersection on a red light, barely missing two

SUVs.

"I'm a little busy right now."

"She's, like, busy right now."

"Give me the phone." Gale took the phone from Katie.

"Change the channel. Go to another website. Don't support broadcast of live car chases. Someone could really get killed."

"That's why they watch, Gale." Katie was right.

Gale continued, "There are innocent people in this car. If the police back off, we'll stop, won't we, Liz?"

"Ah, sure." But I was insincere. At that very moment I was wondering if we could get to Mexico on one tank of gas.

"She said she'd stop if the police cool it."

Katie found another news website. We were live on every TV station and their sister internet site. But only KCAL had us live talking to the anchors.

Gale made our plea. "This has been an innocent misunderstanding gone wrong. Very wrong. All she wants is to sell her script."

All the anchors on the iPad screen laughed. Like that's all any citizen in LA County wanted.

Then Gale made the pitch and said, "*Jane Blonde*, a super-spy who never misses her spa day."

This is where the car chase coverage morphed into a dreamlike "Entertainment Tonight" segment. I heard Gale explaining who she was and saying that she was producing the project and Katie was going to star, as Katie smiled and nodded her approval.

Really? Wow. I could hardly believe my luck. If I'd known that abducting elements like a bankable actress and a prominent producer would convince them to commit to my projects, I would have taken up kidnapping a long time ago.

I was dodging around bumper-to-bumper traffic approaching an intersection when an LA Metro bus rumbled through the light that had just turned red. Just as I hit the brakes, I saw the bus was painted with advertising for an old friend's new movie.

CUT TO THE PAST:

Los Angeles.

Maurice started out as my screenwriting mentor when he had his first movie released. It wasn't a big hit, but it was produced by Disney, so I was impressed. Later he would write blockbusters everyone knew. He warned me before I set foot in California that it would take 10 years to really get established.

We first met before I moved to LA when the software I was using to write scripts ate half my screenplay. His college roommate was the software designer. He sent a bug-free version of the software and input all the missing pages of my script from hard copies. He felt so bad about the disaster that he hooked me up with a screenwriter in LA. That's how I came to know Maurice.

He was gracious enough to read my second script and honest enough to tell me the truth: it really, really sucked. For the next couple of years Maurice gave me notes on scripts and advice about the film business.

When I attended the Selling To Hollywood conference in Glendale, Maurice invited me to come down to Anaheim and go to Disneyland with him. Maurice wrote a Disney movie that had been released the year before. The film was a runaway hit and propelled Maurice to the A-List. It was a giddy time for him.

I moved to LA a few months later, so Maurice and I did a dinner and movie date. I was hopeful that it would be the beginning of a beautiful friendship, or maybe more. We made tentative plans to spend Thanksgiving together, but a family thing came up for him. I hadn't realized he actually had family in LA and neither had he. He'd gotten a call from an old girlfriend letting him know he had a young daughter. He said he had some things to work out. I'll say he did.

After that, I only saw him sporadically. An e-mail here and there, a phone call, a lunch meeting on the DreamWorks campus, where I couldn't help staring at Michael Clarke Duncan, the hulking death row prisoner in *The Green Mile*, a couple tables away.

Maurice was always generous with his time and advice. He had a rarified view from the inside of the Hollywood fortress. His observations were sometimes painful, but always right.

BACK TO THE PRESENT:

West LA.

We dodged the bus advertising Maurice's new pirate movie. I wondered what Maurice would think of my current conundrum. I suddenly realized he may be watching us on TV.

I turned the rearview mirror and checked my makeup. I could not believe my eyes. I was wearing no makeup whatsoever. In my rush to catch the first flight to Vegas, I had spaced on makeup.

Hell-A Rule #41: Never, ever go out of your bedroom without first having your morning facial, plucking your eyebrows, and applying as much makeup as it takes to achieve that natural look.

Good God, here I was with the most TV publicity I'd ever had, and I was pale and colorless except for the red splotches near my left nostril. What if the networks picked this up? What the hell was I thinking? There were no what-ifs involved here. Katie Portman was being kidnapped. We were live on every channel and every news website in every city and town in the world.

"Try CNN.com," I said to Katie, who was watching the iPad screen.

Katie put in the URL. Gale watched over her shoulder.

"Oh my God. We're everywhere. This is unbelievably cool," said Katie. "I'm tweeting this!" Katie logged onto Twitter and tweeted away.

Gale's cell phone rang.

She answered. "Gale."

"Well, we haven't decided on a studio yet, but…"

As I eavesdropped, Gale worked the phone. "Uh huh. Uh huh. Okay. I'll think about it. Gotta go, I've got another call. Gale. Hi, Harvey. Yeah, you're not the only one."

Could that possibly be Harvey Weinstein? I could hear him screaming all the way from New York.

"Okay, Harvey. Sure. Look, I have another call. I'll get back to you. Gale. I have several offers, but we'll put you on the list. No, you can't read the script now. I'll call you later."

As soon as Gale flipped her phone closed, it rang again. She checked the caller ID.

"Universal calling and Warner left a message. So now we know how to sell a project in 10 minutes or less. High-speed pursuit broadcast to the whole country," said Gale.

"The whole world. I just got a tweet from a fan in London and they're watching on BBC!" Katie clapped her hands and squealed. In her bliss, she flipped on the radio to a metal station and started rocking out. Life was getting more surreal by the moment.

"This is a great strategy. You planned this all along, didn't you?" asked Gale.

Not certain who she could be talking to, I glanced back to see her looking straight at me.

"Ah, well, I wish I could say I was that smart," I answered humbly.

Without planning it, we had created heat on *Jane Blonde*. Heat is what it took to sell anything in Hollywood. *Jane* was hot now. I was hot now. We were all hot now. If it weren't for the police being in hot pursuit, the heat would be cool.

I told Gale about Fireball being attached as a producer. At this point, we could have had a Sundance shuttle bus full of indie producers attached and it wouldn't kill the deal. Everybody wanted *Jane* and they wanted her now.

The pigs suddenly sped up. I punched the accelerator. We blew through a busy intersection, running another red light. A flash went off at the corner as a police department surveillance camera took our picture. Katie would be getting a $595 fine in the mail along with a grainy photo of her Bel Air in near collision with a film processing truck.

If I had seen the warning sign that a photo light was coming up, I'm sure I would have automatically swerved onto a side street.

CUT TO THE PAST:

Los Angeles.

When I lived in LA, I charted circuitous courses through the city to avoid encountering any photo lights. I knew too many people who had accidentally run red lights and then received a special delivery the next week from the City of Los Angeles: a terribly unflattering picture of themselves in their car along with an automated ticket for $595, which had to be paid in 10 days or a boot would be locked onto their car wheel if it was parked on a public street.

Once the city discovered that a couple of the automated Got-You-Sucker cameras generated as much revenue in one day as an army of patrol officers could in one month, cameras went up all over LA. I blamed the evil cameras for a bad case of hives I developed the month before we moved back to Florida.

BACK TO THE PRESENT:

West LA.

We swerved around a carload of film students, all with mini-DV cameras shooting the action. Katie gave them a big grin. So there will be at least one film at Slamdance next year "starring" Katie Portman.

My eyes darted to the side mirror. The police cruiser following us veered around the aspiring Scorseses only to clip the rear end of a Mercedes convertible. It was spinning into a minivan when I glanced away.

When I looked back, it was like a demolition derby, one big wreck blocking the intersection. Not one cop car got through.

Ten minutes more and we'd be back on PCH. Planning ahead, I was thinking of finding a way to drive the car onto the beach and right to the tideline. That would be picturesque and no car chase I'd heard of in LA had ended that way. Originality was dissed by the studios but international news loved a pretty ending.

Santa Monica.

Just a block away from the pileup, I spotted a new champagne bar. I was thinking about stopping in for a celebratory toast when I saw the head of the biggest studio in town getting out of a limo with the perfect *Jane Blonde* director, Steven Scott. Yes, the same Steven Scott whom David bought the $1,500 Zegna to impress.

A plan suddenly overtook me. I yanked the emergency brake. The car spun around so fast there was zero sensation of spin. We were suddenly headed in the opposite direction with the engine stalled. Fortunately, at that very moment there was a perfect break in the traffic, and we ended up parked perfectly parallel to the valet station in front of the champagne bar.

Katie squealed with delight. "Awesome!"

A valet rushed to open our doors.

"Nice parking job," the valet said.

I tossed him the keys. "Thanks."

Katie scrambled out, followed by Gale. There was this transformational moment when all three of us realized they were free to escape. We were friends now. I wouldn't have dreamed of shooting them and they knew it. I wouldn't have done it before anyway. That would be a serious waste of much-needed Hollywood female talent.

Gale saw the studio head and Steven Scott stopped at the door of the champagne bar ogling the mega-wreck I had caused down the street.

She gave me an appreciative look. "Smart girl."

Then Gale introduced everyone. The studio head acted like she didn't know me, even though she had bought a six-figure pitch from me a couple years earlier when she was an exec at another studio.

When an exec moves onto another studio, they get project amnesia, forgetting any pitches they took at their former studio and dismissing any scripts they bought as lame. Or maybe I was just one of many unmemorable writers she took advantage of on her way to the top.

Maybe it was best the studio head didn't remember me. The movie never got made. We slipped through the frosted glass doors of the champagne bar together. Obviously, the big studio head didn't have the TV on in her limo.

I overheard Gale whisper to Katie on the way in, "What do you think about Steven? To direct *Jane*, I mean."

Katie gave her a thumbs-up.

I followed the deal inside.

Chapter Fourteen

WHAT'S THE BIG DEAL?

Santa Monica.

It was a tiny place surrounded by walls of polished dark gray cement. Windowless and patronless. An explosion of champagne-colored bubble lights perched on a custom-designed chandelier that crowned an oval bar in the middle of the room. Just what you'd expect for the newest scene in town. Uber-modern, understated elegance with slight echoes of dungeon. Not another patron in sight.

Katie, Gale, Steven, the studio head and I found places at the bar. Without instruction, the bartender popped open a bottle of Cristal that had been waiting in a Waterford crystal bucket of ice. Obviously, the studio had prearranged a private party. Were they closing a deal with Steven? Trying to talk him into directing something he hated? Or maybe Steven did the arranging and he was pitching something.

Even over the jazz of Jean-Luc Ponty piped through tiny surround-sound speakers, I could hear police sirens outside. They neared and then they stopped. The valet driving Katie's Chevy got the scare of his life, no doubt.

Gale had strategically perched on a stool between the director and the studio head at the center of the action.

When Steven asked Gale how she was doing, she said coyly, "Crazy busy."

When he asked what she was working on, she said nothing she could talk about now. This was Hollywood code for "You'll see it in *Variety* next week." It was also provocation for the listener to pry the information out of the talker. Even though she'd blabbed about *Jane Blonde* to millions of TV viewers, she was savvy enough to play hard to get with a veteran like Steven.

But Steven didn't take the bait. He was a pro at shark fishing himself and stopped dead in the water to make a toast as the champagne was poured.

"To life, liberty, and the pursuit of blockbusters."

Everyone laughed and took a sip. I'd never knowingly had champagne this expensive. It was a pale gold and a fountain of tiny bubbles shot up from the bottom of the glass. When you drank it, the little bubbles popped and fizzed in your mouth.

"Wow, this is really, really great," I blurted, sounding like a redneck whose only experience with sparkling was Budweiser and bathroom tile.

No one else commented. They just nodded and smiled. I suddenly realized that I had broken another one of the rules.

Hell-A Rule #42: Never, ever gush.

CUT TO THE PAST:

Hollywood.

The No-Gushing regulation I learned after I met Gary Sinese.

I didn't consider myself a starstruck fan and rarely approached actors even though I saw them on a daily basis. But at the after-party for one of the Cable Ace Awards telecasts, I spotted one of my favorites who had just won an award for his portrayal of Harry Truman in the cable movie "Truman."

I had been a Gary Sinese fan since I saw him in *Of Mice and Men*, an indie film he directed and starred in with John Malkovich. Of course, everyone loved him as Lt. Dan *in Forrest Gump*.

I used the fact that my friend and I had been judges for the Cable Ace Awards as an excuse to embarrass myself, breaking into Sinese's conversation with someone else when there was a lull. I introduced myself and my fellow judge and started the gushathon.

Sinese was gracious and welcomed me as I shook his hand. I didn't lie and say I thought his performance in "Truman" was worthy of an Oscar or any suckup b.s. like that. Instead I said something heartfelt, honest, and over-the-top effusive.

"I loved *Of Mice and Men*. I always use the opening scene with you and Malkovich running across the field to catch the train with the posse and barking dogs on your tail. Oh my God, what a terrific scene," I gushed, spraying a little spit into the air on the word "terrific."

"I use that in writing classes I teach. That scene and the way it was shot create instant sympathy for your characters," I continued, the words spilling out too fast to make sense of them as I got louder and louder. "We don't know what they did, and we don't care what they did, but we're rooting for them to catch that train and get away."

I was almost gasping for breath when I finished with, "And, of course, your performance was so, so wonderful. Just amazing."

My display of vociferous adoration embarrassed everyone within a five-foot radius. But the look on Gary Sinese's face was one of sincere gratitude. He had worked years to get that film made. It wasn't a blockbuster, but it had touched the hearts of moviegoers like myself, and he welcomed my compliment. We chatted for a couple of minutes about what he was working on next and then I excused myself.

Sinese has made many films since then, including *The Green Mile* and *Mission To Mars* and now is a star on "CSI: NY."

As we walked away, my fellow judge said quietly, "Take it down a notch next time, girl. Never let them see you gush."

BACK TO THE PRESENT:

Santa Monica.

Back at the champagne bar, I remembered my friend's advice and shut my mouth about the yummy bubbly. Gale leaned over the bar, looking across Steven and asked me, "So when can you have the next draft?"

Um, did I miss the part where Gale signed a contract with me and gave me notes for the rewrite?

Steven pretended to ignore us, half-turning on his bar stool to act like he was interested in a painting of an impressionistic orgy on the back wall. I was certain he overheard everything we were saying.

"When can you give me notes?" I asked, playing along.

"How about tomorrow?"

"Sure. Then, I can do another pass in…a week or so, depending on your input, of course."

"Perfect. I promised to get a script to Harvey before the end of the month."

Steven could stand it no longer. He swiveled around on his barstool. A little splash of champagne escaped from his glass as he jerked to a halt.

"New project?" Steven asked Gale.

"Right." Gale smiled and then took a graceful sip of the Cristal.

There was a dramatic pause. It could go one way or another. Mr. Scott could take the final step into the invisible trap or he could back away. He took a long sip of his bubbly and said casually, "Don't be so coy. What's the title?"

Gale took an equally dramatic pause and shot a look at me. Then she said, "*Jane Blonde*."

Steven looked her in the eye. "Like James Bond."

"Right. Only think Katie instead of Connery, layer in a little bit of *Charlie's Angels* and *Legally Blonde* and you've got a tentpole."

Tentpole movies were the big blockbusters. The Holy Grails of the film business. A franchise that assured at least two sequels.

Steven remained remarkably calm.

"Sounds interesting."

Suddenly there was a distant boom and then the bar did the shimmy. Another aftershock. It was a little one, maybe 2.8, maybe less, and only lasted about 10 seconds. Everyone feigned coolness, although I noticed Katie's jaw clinched tight.

The studio head, who had been eavesdropping before the boomer, didn't miss a beat and said, "Did you say *Jane Blonde*?"

Gale took another sip of her champagne and nonchalantly said, "Liz's script. It's hot."

The studio head glanced over at Katie. "Are you attached?"

Katie looked at Gale, who nodded.

"If they can, like, work out the numbers," cooed Katie. Smart girl.

There were lots of numbers in Hollywood. Some were good, some were bad. Katie's number would be high and very good. But some numbers were low and very bad, like the number of scripts read at a studio and passed onto executives to consider for a movie.

CUT TO THE PAST:

Jacksonville, Florida.

One in 100 scripts coming into a studio's story department will be recommended for a read by studio production execs. And most of the scripts received by studios are from big agencies and the production companies on the lot.

Where did I get this frightening statistic? From one of the first studio executives I added to my Hollywood contact list. She was head of the story department at Universal and I met her in my Florida hometown before I moved to LA.

The Florida Film Commissioners were having a seminar in Jacksonville and our local film commissioner had asked if I would pick up one of the LA speakers at the airport. As I drove her to her hotel, she said she'd read my script and really liked it.

I knew then she must think I was someone else. I'd never dared send a script directly to any studio, much less a big studio like Universal.

Maybe there was a real writer who was supposed to be picking her up and they couldn't make it. It was one of those dreaded moments when everything stops but the car. My brain froze. My breathing halted. A car horn jolted me out of my gap of suspended animation. I realized the car was drifting into another traffic lane. Not good.

I drifted back into the proper lane hoping the most important person in film I'd ever met wouldn't notice. She did. When I looked over she was gripping the door's armrest. It looked like she was thinking of jumping.

"Oh, sorry. I was just trying to think. I really, actually, don't really remember sending a script to Universal," I said wondering if I was making a mistake admitting it.

"You didn't," she replied. "Judy Dalidge did."

I had sent a script to an acquaintance who moved from Jacksonville to LA.

She was determined to break into the film business as a producer and was reading scripts from anybody. She hadn't told me she had read the script, much less that she liked it, much less she'd passed it on to Universal.

That was one of my first experiences with how things worked in Hollywood. As I said, the writer is the last to know.

I was glad to hear the Universal Bigwig liked my script. However it got there. That was cool. I wasn't sure what to say next. Maybe: "Would you like to buy it?" but before I could ask such a stupid question, Ms. Bigwig said, "So what are you working on now?"

I told her about a high-concept comedy idea that I had been working on. She loved it, she said, and invited me to submit it directly to her at the studio.

What? She didn't want to buy the pitch?

At the time I thought that's how it worked. Write one script. People like it, but maybe don't buy it. So they ask what else you've got. You tell them. They pay you $500,000 to write the script. Maybe she was new to Hollywood and didn't know the drill.

Of course, it was me who was the novice. Shortly after that I was thrust into the jaws of the beast and my survival depended on my quick assimilation of the Tao of Hollywood. I met Tao and I kicked its ass.

BACK TO THE PRESENT:

Santa Monica.

The studio head gulped down the last of her champagne and turned to Gale. "You have a deal yet?"

Another tremor rattled the glasses hanging upside down over the bar. The barkeep stepped back. Everyone else grabbed their champagne glasses to steady them. No one seemed anxious except Katie. It stopped. Katie giggled, a burst of nervous hee-haw.

"We promised to give the Weinsteins a first look. And Universal, Dream-Works and Warner called not five minutes ago."

"Uh huh. What can I do to convince you to bring it to us first?"

The bar phone rang. The bartender answered. As Gale worked the studio head, I overheard the bartender say, "Hostages. Yeah, right. That's a good one." He laughed and hung up.

"What's the story?" The studio head leaned toward Gale eager to hear the pitch.

Gale looked over at me. "Liz?"

I stole her line and said, "She's a super spy who never misses her spa day."

Everyone laughed, including the studio head, who squirmed off her stool. She grabbed her champagne and headed toward the back of the room.

Everyone followed her to a booth. Charcoal-grey leather covered the seats. The table looked like some kind of slate.

"Tell me more." The studio head had just convened a pitch meeting.

Even though I hadn't pitched *Jane Blonde* in over three months, the story began spilling out in a torrent of action sequences. In the background, I barely noticed the phone ringing again. I took a beat at the perfect time in the pitch and glanced over at the bartender, who was glancing over at us. I heard him say, "You must be shitting me."

Then I hit the third act hard and brought it all home to the resolution in the mandatory 15-minute story binge. When I finished, there was a moment of silence around the table. In my experience, a moment of silence was a really good call-business-affairs-to-draft-a-deal-memo sign. Or a really bad drink-poisioned-absynthe-and-die sign.

The studio head was first to speak. "That's really…wonderful." She studied me a moment. "Have we worked with you before?"

"Ah, no, but I sold a pitch to Fox and…"

Katie interrupted by saying, "Her grandfather is Ray Bradbury."

"Well, not…" I didn't get my honest clarification started when the studio head said, "The pitch to Fox, what was it called and what's the status?"

Hell-A Rule #43: Never remind anyone you've met before that they should know you, especially if they paid you $150,000 for a script.

I pretended to forget that she was the exec who bought the pitch and said, "It's called *Return of the Sweet Birds*. A comedy about a Motown girl band from the '60s that gets back together for a reunion tour. Only problem is, they hate each other's guts."

"Like Diana Ross and The Supremes," the studio head said.

"Right."

"It didn't get made, so is it in turnaround?" she asked.

Turnaround means Studio One buys something hot like a script and decides later whatever they bought is not so hot. Then maybe Studio Two comes along and thinks the script is actually pretty hot and buys it from Studio One, then puts the film into pre-production.

"Well, I'm not sure," I lied. I was. It wasn't.

"Did you have any attachments?" the studio head asked.

"Danny Glover and BabyFace Edmonds," I answered.

She thought for a moment, searching her brain's RAM for a clue. "*Sweet Birds*. Now I remember. I bought that just before I left Fox."

She didn't apologize for not remembering me or my project. She didn't even look embarrassed.

"You wrote that with Glover's producer. She's your writing partner?"

"Well, we wrote *Sweet Birds* and have a couple other things circulating in town. I'm solo now."

CUT TO THE PAST:

Los Angeles.

I had met Danny Glover's producer when we were both judging the Cable Ace Awards. She's my friend who warned me about the No-Gush Rule after meeting Gary Sinese. I called her my Carolina Angel, since she came into my life when I desperately needed a studio deal, and she was a southern girl from South Carolina.

Angel and I collaborated on the Sweet Birds story, her original idea. We pitched it to Danny Glover on the Warner Brothers lot on the *Lethal Weapon 4* set.

Pitching was a joyous thing to me, but I had never pitched to an actor whose face I'd seen in extreme closeup on the silver screen. To avoid getting lock-brained, I rehearsed the pitch to a picture of Danny Glover taped to my living room chair.

What I wasn't prepared for was that I didn't pitch to Danny Glover, actor. It was Murtaugh, detective from the *Lethal Weapon* movies. He had his badge clipped to his belt and everything. Fortunately, the prop master had relieved Detective Murtaugh of his lethal weapon before lunch. When he came bounding into his trailer, I was struck by his size and graciousness.

Danny Glover was a big guy, 6'2" or so. When Angel introduced us, he made me feel like a long-lost sister, even though I was the only white-skinned soul in his personal sanctuary. Some friends who were waiting to see Glover left. He ate his lunch quickly as we pitched our hearts out.

Angel warned me Glover would take a couple of weeks to decide whether he wanted to produce *Sweet Birds*. We hadn't created a role for him as an actor because Angel assumed, based on their slate of projects, he would only be interested in producing.

Our pitch and Glover's lunch ended simultaneously. He wiped his mouth with his napkin and said, "I love it. Let's do it."

Angel and I sat there a moment, stunned.

"Only thing is," Glover pushed his plate aside and took a long drink of spring water, "I want a role."

Angel and I created a part for Glover. It was a record producer who had been the former road manager of the feuding divas. The original Motown recording company that launched the Sweet Birds was almost bankrupt and Glover's character had to find them, figure out how to get them back on the road and save the record company.

We met with him again. He loved the role we created for him and quickly had some deep insights into his character. With Danny Glover firmly attached as a producer and star, William Morris, Glover's agency, jumped aboard the bullet train known as *Sweet Birds*.

Agents don't stand at stations waiting for a project to pull in so they can step on in a civil manner, expecting no other agents to be aboard. They like to gallop alongside a runaway project headed to the studios, like Old West train robbers, and launch themselves toward it, hoping they will ride long enough to get 10 per cent of the deal.

The Morris boys reconfirmed everything I'd heard about big-agency agents. Short attention spans, soulless personalities, and all of them possessed God-complexes. They were also very good at their jobs.

When we went into Morris's plush El Camino Drive offices for a pitch meeting, the last word of our 17-minute story was barely out of my mouth when the lead agent blurted out, "Too long. Fifteen minutes or less."

Nothing about how he liked the story or characters or anything. Angel asked what he thought. He said, "They'll buy it." Then he left the room.

Shortly afterward, Angel and I pitched the story to BabyFace Edmonds' film company, they loved it and jumped aboard as producers. It wouldn't hurt for them to do the music, either.

With *Sweet Birds*, I was the smallest part of the project from the agency's point of view. I was being hip-pocketed again and I knew it. I mentioned signing with Morris to Angel, but she said she wouldn't worry about it. She assumed the agents working with us just assumed I would sign with the agency when the *Sweet Birds* deal was done.

I consulted Zen Man. He said, "One cannot see their path if they rush through the fog." I took that to mean I should be patient making my way through the Hollywood smog.

A writer friend heard about my plight and referred me to his agent at ICM, another literary/talent agency giant. She read me, said she loved me, and invited me to sign on the dotted line.

Another agent raiding the money train.

When I talked to Zen Man about the William Morris guys ignoring me and ICM offering to sign me, he said, "The bird that leaves his prey to capture another field mouse is a hungry bird." Yeah, but what about the path and the fog?

I wasn't totally clear about the mouse and bird metaphor, but it sounded like I had his blessing to sign with ICM.

I signed, we pitched the Sweet Birds story with Danny Glover and Baby-Face attached to Fox. They bought it. It took six long months to negotiate the deal and get all the contracts signed. I got my first big studio check the same day I met my true love and almost husband-to-be at the Women in Film soiree.

BACK TO THE PRESENT:

Santa Monica.

The studio head said, "I always liked the *Sweet Birds* project. Too bad it never got made."

Everyone nodded sympathetically, as if I should be in mourning or something. Like my baby never got to grow up and play with other movies on opening weekend.

Then the studio head eyed Gale. "And you've got the *Jane Blonde* script?" Meaning, did Gale have an option or at least a verbal agreement from my people that she would be attached as producer? Of course, she didn't.

"Yes," she fibbed.

"You've actually read the script and it's good?" Then realizing I probably heard that, she glanced at me and said, "No offense, of course."

I should've said, "No offense taken. I'm a Hollywood writer and we're used to abuse." But I just nodded and tried to smile.

I noticed the bartender hanging up the phone and sneaking toward the back door. I checked the front door. No SWAT yet. We probably had two minutes.

"It's not good, it's terrific," Gale testified, even though I didn't think she had even read a word of the script. Yes, she took it to studios, but her people would have done the heavy reading.

Katie leaned over the table. "It's funny, poignant and really kicks ass."

Hell-A Rule #44: A project becomes much more interesting if others are interested in it. Mass buying hysteria and bidding wars can be created by a couple of the right people sniffing around the project.

Everyone in unison took a gulp of Cristal.

The studio head locked eyes with Steven. "Would you be interested?"

"I'd have to read it." That was Hollywood-speak for "Hell, yes."

I heard the back door slam shut and shouting somewhere behind the building. Then the engine whine of heavy armored vehicles pulling up front.

"Listen, if you agree to do *Jane Blonde*, we could let that Matson & Abner thing go."

Matson & Abner? Ah, the circle of life in Hollywood.

He looked like he'd just been given a reprieve. He nodded, trying not to let the elation show.

The studio head's cell phone rang. She grabbed it from her bag, checked the incoming number, and turned it to mute.

"Who's your agent? Weren't you at Morris or CAA?" The studio head looked over at me.

"When you were at Fox, I was with ICM and then Paradigm. But after that I signed with Mark Wald and Jeff Skelly, but they broke up..." As I rambled on, I noticed the smell of boredom wafting through the air.

"And then I signed with Nevison, but I just left them today." Left them in shambles, trembling in the street.

Gale jumped in, "I'm hooking her up at ICM." Then she remembered I was actually in the room with them and turned to me, "I mean, if you would like. Or if you'd like to go back to CAA, I can make a call."

I nodded.

Gale's cell, Katie's cell and Steven's cell all went off almost simultaneously. They each checked the numbers and followed the studio head's lead, turning their phones to mute.

I heard a muffled commotion out front. No one else seemed to notice.

"Gale, so you'll produce?"

Gale pretended to think about it. "Yes, if Steven will direct."

The studio head glanced at Steven, while he pretended to think about it.

"Yes, if my company can co-produce and Katie will star. I'm certain we can work out a deal."

Gale nodded.

A third aftershock rumbled through the joint. The bubble-light chandelier swayed. Behind the bar, a glass broke.

"Two point five." Everyone agreed.

Katie smacked her hand on the table and shrieked, "I wish this would stop."

No one knew what to say.

Katie's eyes darted toward the door, as if she wanted to flee the building before an earthquake tore it down around her.

"Sorry. I've lived here, like, all my life and I still hate those things."

The studio head leaned across the table and said, "We all do, honey." She patted Katie's hand sympathetically. "Do we have a deal?"

There was a horrible moment, like a freeze frame in a film scene, where no one moved or spoke. In that 10 seconds a panicked message popped up in my brain's in-box: *Oh my God, it's happening again. A major motion picture was blowing up in my face.*

All eyes were on Katie, whose trepidation about earthquakes was overtaken by a brilliant career move. She sat up straight in the booth and seemed to magically be composed again.

She thrust her hand across the table to shake with the studio head. "Blonde. Jane Blonde." Then she laughed really loud. Everyone joined her in a drunken jubilee of anticipated blockbuster success.

Nobody asked me, but I was only the owner of the copyright. I'm sure they were sure they could hook me up with an agent, who would convince me he had my best interest at heart, when in fact he had no heart and would sell my project for whatever price the studio dictated.

"Deal." Everyone shook hands with everyone else and the studio head looked for the bartender to order more champagne.

I gulped down the sparkly in my glass, becoming besotted with Cristal and the promise of dizzying overnight success. After 10 years of slaving away in the noxious, oppressive mines of Hollywood, I was ready for triumph.

I barely made out a barely audible voice outside say through a loudspeaker, "Come out with your hands up or we're coming in."

Again, no one else seemed to hear it, or being from LA, they'd heard it too many times for it to pierce their real-time awareness.

The studio head noticed the bartender was MIA.

"Where'd he go?" She got up to investigate while Gale, Steven, and Katie speculated on where they'd like to go to shoot the movie.

I volunteered, "The story is set in London, New Zealand, and LA."

"London's good and we all love New Zealand, don't we?" Steven said. Everyone smiled.

I glanced back toward the bar, where the studio head was wrestling the cork out of another bottle of Cristal.

The sound of the cork popping coincided with an ear-splitting explosion near the front door. A flash-bang flash-banging.

It was like a scene from one of Steven's movies — we all ducked instinctively, covering our heads. As the studio head dropped behind the bar for cover, a plague of SWAT commandos invaded our space.

We sat stunned, surrounded by adrenaline, testosterone and itchy trigger-fingers. The Head Poo-bah yapped orders. Instead of sounding like George C. Scott in *Patton*, he sounded like PeeWee Herman in a porn theatre.

"Everyone down. Down on the floor!" he commanded in a squeaky cartoon voice. Not very convincing.

There was a moment of transcendental silence and Steven started laughing, looking over at the studio head as she rose from behind the bar.

"Good one. Were you planning to incarcerate me until I agreed to direct that bloody movie of yours?"

He took a gulp of champagne and continued, "Who the hell cast SWAT No.1? They should be beheaded."

"On…the…floor." The Chihuahua-on-helium voice was more deliberate and louder.

One of the officers grabbed me by the arm, yanking me out of the booth. I was kissing the floor with his knee in my back in one nanosecond. Gale was next. A handsome SWAT hunk took her down.

We were eye to eye being handcuffed when she said to me, "They are so sued."

"Cut! Cut! Cut, damn it!" Steven leapt out of the booth, flailing his arms like directors do. A commando introduced him to the floor.

Then I heard Pee Wee Commando say, "It's Katie Portman!"

I glanced up to see Katie slide out of the booth and smile that $15 million smile. "Do you think this is, like, really necessary?"

They arrested us and booked us into the Beverly Hills jail. That answered that question.

Chapter Fifteen

SLAMMER 90210

Beverly Hills.

I was glad Beverly Hills PD took precedence since the whole adventure started in their fair city. They had the plushest cells in the metro area. The City Hall/Jail/Library complex was familiar territory to me, although the jail part was a new experience.

It was more like a Ritz-Carlton with tiny rooms than any jail cell I'd seen. The mini bar didn't have wine, but it did have Odwalla Vitamin C Protein Drink and three kinds of designer water. The smallish bed was covered in 1000-thread-count Egyptian cotton sheets with hand-embroidered pillows. The furnishings were sparse, but I swear everything was custom-made maple and stainless steel.

There was plenty of time to contemplate my future or lack of it from my cell. Would I be sent to Attica or Folsom? I didn't even know if they were still open for "business." Could I be transferred to Florida where Christopher could come visit me on the weekends if he was still speaking to me? Would I end up in Lowell Women's Prison and morph into a bull dyke?

But wait. Maybe I could plead insanity. After all, I gave up a high-paying job in Paradise to come to Hell-A to be treated like a migrant filmworker. If that wasn't proof of madness, I didn't know what was.

Didn't I at least get a phone call? Where were the guards?

I peeked out of the little window in the door. All I saw was a wall painted in a fashionable khaki color, framing the same Dante's Hell painting as hung in Nevison's lobby. Screaming faces started my day of wild abandon and ended it, too.

I sat down on my little bed, wondering if Christopher had already moved out of the house we shared or was he on a plane to LA to rescue me?

Then I started thinking about my family in Florida. Had they seen the whole thing on CNN? Would Christopher have thought to tell them, since it was obvious from his last phone call he'd been watching? I'm sure my Uncle Richard in Daytona Beach had seen it live. He is a CNN/Fox News junkie. All the bad news all the time. He rarely goes out of the house when a disaster is happening. He gets all hopped up on adrenaline from 24/7 disaster coverage.

CUT TO THE PAST:

Florida.

Uncle Richard was a big influence in my life and encouraged me to pursue artistic endeavors. He set me on the path toward becoming a Suffering Artist when I was 5 years old and he taught me how to draw. He introduced me to the voice of Barbra Streisand when I was 8.

Having grown up with twangy country & western music I loathed, Streisand's vocals were a shock to my ears. I can still recall standing there, not being able to speak, somehow realizing I was having a life-changing moment.

And then I discovered rock on the radio.

In a way, Streisand and rock were responsible for changing my path in the world. Instead of settling into the comfortable life of a genteel white girl growing up in a small southern town, safe and boring, I wanted adventure.

Quickly, I wasn't satisfied with just listening to rock, I wanted to play rock. So at the chaotic age of 13, I joined a rock band. To my mother's credit, she gave her blessing to my wild idea and allowed me to buy a keyboard and speakers with money I'd earned making window signs for shops on Main Street.

When the inevitable falling out happened over creative differences and I quit the band in a melodramatic tantrum, I talked my mom into allowing me to move to Central Florida, where my grandparents lived. I moved into the third-story attic of the boarding house my grandmother owned in DeLand. I painted the walls black and joined another rock band. I was in and out of bands until I was 21. I then sold my equipment, hung up my rock star attitude, and went to apprentice with my Uncle Richard in his commercial art studio in Jacksonville.

It was music and art that saved me from trailer parks and laundromats. It was chronic curiosity that saved me from a life spent wondering how things would have turned out if I had been braver.

BACK TO THE PRESENT:

Beverly Hills.

I had learned that in Hollywood, bravery got mixed up with madness a lot. Was it courage that had kept me in Hell-A or was it delusion?

The sound of footsteps echoed in the hallway outside my cell door. There was a click and the door came unlocked. A tiny female officer swung the door open.

"You may have your phone call now," said Tiny.

I rose from the bed and said, "Excellent. I need to call my publicist."

It was supposed to be a joke, but she didn't laugh. Probably because it sounded like a reasonable thing in Hollywood. We walked to the end of the hall where a wall phone hung in an alcove. There was a built-in bench of stainless steel.

I sat down and Officer Tiny stood by patiently.

My brain went all foggy like early mornings in winter on the beach in Florida. I couldn't remember Zen Man's phone number. Why would I? It was on speed dial at home. Or should I call Christopher first?

I looked out at Tiny and said, "Only one call?"

"One," she replied, studying her artificial fingernails decorated with signs of the Zodiac.

I turned back to the phone. I needed my PDA. I should call Zen Man and have him call Christopher. Zen Man could find a criminal defense attorney for me. He would come and visit. But what was his number?

"Do you have a phone book?"

Officer Tiny turned and grabbed a phone directory from a built-in shelf in the hallway. She handed it to me.

I flipped to the business section and searched for Zen Man's firm. It wasn't there. I turned to the Yellow Pages and scanned the attorney's section. Nope. Then I checked the front cover. Beverly Hills. Zen Man was in Venice Beach. That would probably be in a West LA phone book.

"Do you have West LA?"

Tiny looked down her nose at me. "No. You have five minutes."

Okay. So the choice was made for me. I had to call Christopher and have him call Zen Man. I picked up the phone and my mind went blank. I couldn't remember Christopher's work number. It was on speed-dial at home. There were some 2s and a 4.

I put in the area code. Then my finger trembled as I punched in the rest of the numbers, praying they were right.

After a couple of rings, a woman answered in a raspy voice, "Heller." That's hello in Deep South English.

My heart sank. It wasn't Christopher's work. But I said, "Is Christopher there?"

"Nope," she said and then there was a dial tone.

I started to dial again, but Tiny stopped me.

"Only one call."

She seized my arm and pulled me up. I grabbed the phone receiver and held on for dear life.

"It was a wrong number."

"Doesn't matter." Tiny tried to separate me from the phone, but my arms were longer than hers and I had about 25 pounds on her.

"What we've got here is failure to communicate," I said, hoping she would find the *Cool Hand Luke* quote funny. She didn't.

"I have to call my boyfriend," I pleaded as I tried to get loose from her grip.

We struggled for a few moments. And then suddenly Officer Tiny gave up. I thought she was going to give me a break. Instead she gave me a blast of pepper spray.

It felt like my eyes were on fire. I screamed and fell to the floor, blinded from the attack. I held my hands to my eyes, hoping the pepper spray wouldn't eat into my brain. I moaned and wailed as I heard mean Tiny radio for back-ups.

"There is no pain. There is no pain," I repeated in my mind.

I heard a door slam not far away and then the sound of someone running toward us. Suddenly a pair of hands that were definitely male jerked me up to my feet.

"Let's go," a deep voice said. I wasn't certain if it was male or female.

I stumbled along, still suffering from the spray. "I can't see. I'm blind."

We stopped, I heard a door open and the officer pushed me through. I thought it was my cell. The officer hauled me across the little room until I ran into something. It was about waist high and maybe metal. Definitely not my suite.

"Bend over," said the officer.

"What?" Oh, Jesus, I tried to avoid seeing prison movies because they were so depressing, but I knew what happened when you bent over.

Then I heard water running in front of me.

"Bend over and open your eyes," commanded the officer. "We have to wash out the pepper spray."

After a few minutes of irrigation, I could see again. The officer, a linebacker of a woman, ushered me back to my cell.

I plopped down on the bed and put my feet up. Why, oh, why did I think this would work out for the best? Here I was 3,000 miles from home, the subject of police brutality and totally alone. I wondered if Christopher would figure out where I was. I thought about Zen Man. He would surely be here any minute, wouldn't he?

These were the times when a soul felt the value of family.

CUT TO THE PAST:

Florida.

The largest sacrifice I made during those eight terrible years living in LA was not spending time with my dad, my grandpa, and great-grandmother before they passed away. All three went to heaven while I chased down my Hollywood dream.

Hell-A Rule #45: Family first, unless you're writing a studio film on assignment, meeting with an A-List star about starring in your movie, or accepting an Oscar for surviving the torture chamber called Hollywood.

My dad was the first to go over. He had a heart attack at the flea market where he spent every Saturday morning. He fell between the parked cars and no one found him until it was too late. But through the miracles of modern stupidity, he was revived and put on life support, even though his brain was dead. I wept openly on the plane as I flew home. The flight attendants tried to quiet me with champagne. I only got worse.

My half brothers and I gave our consent to disconnect all the scary machines. He had carried a card in his wallet for years requesting that he not be revived if his body gave out, although the paramedics found no card on the day they were called to his rescue. He would have been mad as hell to see himself there, puffy, and at the mercy of bleeping electronics.

The last time I had visited was at Christmas. It was one of the few overnight visits to his tiny apartment in Central Florida. We had breakfast at IHOP, as he had done for decades. He talked about his Living Legends Hall of Fame award and the parade he'd ridden in that summer with the other veteran NASCAR drivers. Then we drove over to Daytona to the flea market.

After he bought me a Christmas decoration, we headed over to the Speedway. He turned into the entrance and we did a lap around the Speedway parking lot. Dad would always say the same thing, "Man, oh man, look at those Winston stands now. Remember when I took you and your mother to the 500? When was that?"

I always had the same reply, "I don't know. A few years ago." After he died,

I found the souvenir program he bought for us. It was 1989.

Then Dad saw an old friend parked across the lot and stopped to talk. I stayed in the air conditioning while they shook hands and caught up on the good times. When I asked Dad if he was an old racing buddy, he replied, "That was Bill France."

Bill France Sr. was the godfather of NASCAR. He passed away shortly after we saw him that day. "He was a great man," my father said when he called me to say his friend had died.

Two months later, Dad went to the big speedway in the sky.

In a daze, I made it through the funeral, which was attended by a NASCAR official and relatives I never knew. Buick sent a dozen cars to carry mourners in a dazzling parade of shiny new Roadmasters to the Oakdale Cemetery. It had been years since my dad sold his Buick dealership, yet someone remembered him. I was grateful.

About a year after Dad passed, my sweet grandpa joined him. I had been close with Daddy Jodie, as we called him. He spoiled us when we were kids, took me in to live with my grandma and him when I was 17, and gave me my first job at his butcher shop. When I lived in Florida I drove down to see him about every two months, but when I moved to Hell-A, I only saw him during my annual pilgrimage home, usually at Christmas. He fell ill and I called him everyday. I sent flowers when he was in the hospital. I had a plane ticket to go see him, but he couldn't wait. He passed away before we could say goodbye.

My great-grandmother, Mae, died at 92 shortly after Grandpa. They were from two different branches of the family and had never even met. Mae was an inspiration.

One Christmas Eve while the family gathered for present distribution, Mae was out in her yard mowing the lawn on her new John Deere riding mower. Everyone was against its purchase for fear she would fall off and the thing would run over her. But she insisted she had to have one before she died.

As we watched her there through my mother's sliding glass windows, the light was failing, and the headlamps of the John Deere blinked on. Just as this happened, in full view of uncles, aunts, cousins, and preachers, Mae plowed into a camellia bush as tall as the mower. The front left wheel tilted up, breaking down half the bush, and the razor- sharp blades shredded the shrub in a shower of green and pink. As we piled out of the sliding glass door, she had mowed down a pecan sapling, a row of zinnias and smashed into the old potting shed.

Unfazed, she climbed off the mower, grabbed her presents off the porch and herded us all back to my mom's for Christmas gift exchange. I admired Mae's spunk and resilience. She was like the EverReady Bunny, going and going, until finally her batteries ran out.

On the hat tree in my Beverly Hills apartment I kept my dad's last NAS-CAR cap, my grandpa's old felt fedora and a straw sun hat Mae wore to go fishing. One of the reasons Christopher and I decided to move back to Florida was the hats. I feared my mom's would be added to the collection soon.

After returning to Florida, I added another loved one's hat to the hat tree: Bill Kelley's Irish tartan plaid cap.

A few months after we left California, Bill's wife, Nina, called to say he passed away. He'd been diagnosed with cancer a couple of months earlier and refused to tell his friends. He was sure he would win the fight. But Wild Bill Kelley stormed heaven in a rage of glory even before any of us knew he was sick.

I sat there on the phone, the words numbing me. I was suddenly ejected into a world of nothingness. I felt nothing, heard nothing. The sky was blank.

I think Nina talked some more and I may have said I was so sorry. But it was someone else saying those empty words, not me. I was with Bill somewhere in the past the last time we saw each other working on a polish of *The Tyree Legend* script.

We'd finished that draft and given it to my agent at ICM, Agent Black. She was no fan of crime drama unless it had a Disney ending, so nothing much happened with the script. It went through a couple of name changes from *The Tyree Legend* to *Murder on the Hudson* to *The River and The Knife*, oh, and Agent Black's least favorite — *The Doeskin Murders*.

I am confident that one day *The Tyree Legend* will be made into a movie and Bill will win his second Academy Award. I'm sorry to say he won't be there to accept it.

He was a Keeper of the Word, a Keeper of the Gates, a Keeper of the Flame.

I miss my dear co-conspirator and am certain of one thing: God has his hands full.

BACK TO THE PRESENT:

Beverly Hills.

The biggest sacrifice I had made to pursue the madness of a career in screenwriting was losing my loved ones. Now, sitting in my cell feeling sorry for myself, I wondered if it was worth it.

It was late afternoon when I heard voices and footsteps coming down the hall. They stopped at my door. Once again, my jailers swung open the door.

Tiny said, "Your bail has been paid. You're free to go."

"What…I mean, who paid my bail?" I asked as I hurried to the door.

"One of the studios."

The amazon officer eyed me and asked, "Are you a famous writer?"

"I probably am now," I replied, as I took my grateful self out of that hell-hole.

Tiny grasped my elbow to escort me to freedom.

Amazon followed close behind and said, "You know, I've been writing a screenplay. It takes place in a women's prison. It's a comedy."

Good Lord in heaven, please send me back to Florida where only 50 percent of the population is writing a screenplay.

"Sounds promising," I fibbed.

"Would you like to read it?" asked Amazon.

We came to a steel door. Tiny punched in numbers on a key pad and inserted a key card. The door slid open.

"Send it to my agents."

Tiny escorted me through the door. Amazon stayed behind.

As the door was sliding shut, Amazon shouted to me, "Who are your agents?"

"Dopey and Grumpy," I answered.

The studio made quick work of the bond details. But instead of being released onto the gritty streets of Beverly Hills immediately, I was "invited" to a studio "debriefing." Sort of like when Special Forces come home from a mission.

Tiny led me to a room with double doors. When she swung one open, I stepped in to find Gale, Katie, the studio head, Steven and every attorney representing every party involved in the huge *Jane Blonde* deal in the room, including my beloved Zen Man and Fireball, who jumped up to hug me when I came in.

The biggest surprise guests were Fifi and Pammy, Katie's minder. The only players missing from our afternoon soiree at the Portman mansion were David, Jason, Hugh, and his Unidentified Friend.

It was a huge conference room with a 15-foot-long maple and stainless steel table in the middle. On the khaki/sage green walls were tasteful photo portraits of some of Beverly Hills' most famous former citizens — Jimmy

Stewart, Marilyn Monroe, Gregory Peck, and Carrot Top — all lighted by perfect pin lights in the ceiling.

Sometimes deals and projects take years to set up and move through the Hollywood system. *Jane Blonde* took one adrenaline-charged afternoon.

I sat between Zen Man and Fireball at a shiny conference table for 20. Zen Man leaned over and whispered, "Are you all right, honey?"

Even at the most high-pitched business moment, Zen Man was attuned to the human soul inside his client/friends.

"Are you kidding?" I couldn't help laughing. I was sitting at a table with Hollywood sovereigns and their attorneys ready to seal the biggest deal of my crazy screenwriting career — at least that's what I was thinking. Why wouldn't I be all right?

Yes, we were still in the Beverly Hills Police Station. Yes, I had a couple of minute criminal charges to cope with: evading arrest, reckless driving, leaving the scene of an accident, assault with a deadly weapon — oh yeah, and kidnapping and attempted murder.

I wondered if Gloria Allred would take my case and speculated how a Coffee Bean Iced Mocha defense would play in a Beverly Hills courtroom.

I was loving life.

Hell-A Rule #46: Bad is good, good is best and mean justifies the happy ending.

An army of agents, managers and publicists filed into the room and sat behind their clients. I almost gasped when I saw my former agent, Jason, stroll in with the Nevison Agency head.

David was absent. Carrying on social intercourse with nurses at Cedars-Sinai, no doubt. I hoped the surgery to remove the 9mm slug from his foot was painful.

I leaned over and whispered to Zen Man, "What are they doing here? I'm not repped by them anymore."

Zen Man patted my wrist. "I know. We had to kiss them into the deal to get them to be more understanding about your…ah…meeting with them earlier today. Don't stress. Sparrows always fight over the fat worm."

Was he calling me a fat worm? Or was I one of the sparrows?

One of the most famous young agents in town stopped at my chair and bent down to introduce himself. Of course, I knew who he was. Everyone did, including Gale, who had plans to hook me up with another agency. She eyed my new agent with malice. Without a conflict of interest, she would have to pay a hell of a lot more for *Jane.*

Fireball whispered, "I thought Stars&Lit was a good place for you. And Zach can help with the deal, if you like him. Of course, there are others."

"That's cool. I like him."

Zach, the hot agent, parked himself in a chair behind me. Everyone in the room nodded to him, grinning, except Jason and his boss. They had to be kicking themselves in their egos at the moment, having lost the most valuable client in their stable.

Pow-wows around the table took the noise level to opening-night-at-the-new-scene-restaurant intensity, until the door swung open and in walked a George Clooney look-alike in a Beverly Hills cop uniform. He stood authoritatively at the head of the table until everyone became mute.

"Good afternoon, ladies and gentlemen, I'm Police Chief Walker ,and I want to say on behalf of everyone in our department what a privilege it is to have you all here."

I was confused. I thought I had been arrested. He made it sound like some awards ceremony or celebrity roast. Already the Young Turks circling the room were getting impatient, checking text messages, logging onto their favorite porn sites.

Chief W. cleared his throat and continued, "I just wanted to clarify a few points. All charges have been dropped by all parties involved."

He paused a moment for dramatic effect. He must have taken acting lessons at the local Y. Or maybe he expected a round of applause or a jubilant outburst. He got neither.

"Although, I cannot guarantee civil law suits will not be filed by motorists or pedestrians impacted by vehicular violations committed by anyone present." He looked straight at me. I studied an unfortunate hangnail trying to decide whether it would bleed too much if I bit it off.

The studio head cleared her throat and pointedly checked her watch so everyone in the room would notice, including Chief W. He ignored her.

"I would like to say that I and my officers sincerely regret any unnecessary physical force experienced by anyone during the arrest process. I'm sure you must all know the Beverly Hills Police Department's foremost concern is the safety of our citizens and I apologize for any…"

The studio head rose to her feet ominously. "Thank you, Chief Walker. We sincerely appreciate your concern and consideration. I can assure you no police abuse charges will be filed against your fine men and I'm certain you will excuse us while we convene our urgent meeting."

She brought the meeting to order as Chief W. stood, stunned by the abrupt ending of his big speech before world-famous celebrities and their leeches. No doubt he had prepared a rousing final remark to inspire any producers in the room to hire him as a consultant for their next buddy cop movie.

Poor Chiefy sulked out the door. He turned for a moment and said half-heartedly, "If there's anything I can do for you…"

I may have been the only one who heard him, since everyone else was in the thick of general deal points already. It took all of five minutes. Everyone was on the same page. Everyone was in the same ballpark. Greed permeated the air, filling our lungs with good cheer.

After we reached an agreement about what we would all be telling the press—that my hostage-taking rampage was just one well-orchestrated publicity stunt for *Jane Blonde*—we all adjourned to the front steps of the police station, where dozens of media vultures and paparazzi gathered.

I stood there marveling at the squirming sea of hungry reporters and their camera crews. All the 24-hour news stations were there along with LA's local guys, but the big surprise was the Japanese and Latin press. I even spotted a BBC logo.

All right, Mr. Stone, I'm ready for my close-up.

One reporter called out, "Liz, were you alone in the kidnappings?"

Before I could answer, the studio head addressed the media, announcing the deal and explaining that yes, indeed, it was all an elaborate publicity stunt.

Another reporter shouted out, "Liz, were you actually willing to risk your life to sell your script? Was this really a publicity stunt?"

I couldn't lie to the media, so I stepped forward, thrust my fist in the air and did a Howard Dean scream, "Power to the screenwriters."

There was a moment of bewildered silence, then one reporter started clapping.

I suddenly realized I had accidentally created the worst cliché in movies, the slow clapping scene, where the hero gets up in front of a crowd and says something profound, then one person claps, then another until the whole group is cheering and applauding wildly. I hate those scenes. I held my breath hoping like hell that didn't happen.

It didn't. The lone reporter looked embarrassed and stopped clapping. The media went on to interview anyone who wanted to be interviewed, including Fireball, the Chief of Police and even Fifi and Pammy. The impromptu pre-production press junket went on for almost two hours. Later marketing gurus and studio execs alike would call the whole thing "genius." The studio and A-List elements took credit and I took a fat check to the bank.

Zen Man gave me a ride to the parking garage where I had left my rental truck.

I gave him a thank-you hug.

"Don't ever do anything like that again."

"Are you kidding? I've already got my next crime spree planned for *Jane Blonde II*. This time we'll crash the studio gates, storm the executive building, and put the whole place under siege."

"Who's we?"

"Jane and I, of course."

I blew him a kiss as he sped away in his Mini Cooper S.

The truck was still there with a brand new parking ticket on the windshield. As I plucked the citation from under the windshield wiper, I noticed a grenade I accidentally left on the seat of the truck.

Clearly, the parking enforcement officer was phoning it in, an acting term meaning he or she was just going through the motions with little passion or attention to detail. Nobody loved their job anymore, especially parking officers in LA.

I hopped in, drove to the cashier's booth to find that I owed the maximum day rate, since I exceeded the hourly rate break of four hours. I forked over $15 gladly, counting myself lucky that SWAT hadn't discovered the "perp's" vehicle and impounded it.

When I was arrested, the police officers found my cell phone in Katie's car. It was returned to me when I was released so as soon as I got a decent cell signal, I phoned home. It was 7 p.m. in LA, 10 p.m. in Florida. The answering machine picked up and Christopher's voice said: "Liz, if you're calling me, I'm on the way to LA. Call my cell phone."

A rush of joy swept over my heart. Christopher hadn't left me, he was coming to save me. How romantic is that?

I dialed his cell phone. It rang twice and then he picked up.

"Liz, where are you?"

"In Beverly Hills," I answered.

Then he continued, "Do you realize what I've been going through? First I wake up to a note about you going to LA on vacation. Then I get your voice mail message at work. Then you call to say you've kidnapped your agents. Then Bridgette from advertising tells me there's a hostage standoff in Beverly Hills and she thinks you're the kidnapper. The whole staff is gathered round this one TV at the office. I can't believe what I'm seeing — you driving some old American car…"

"It was a '57 Chevy Bel Air. A classic."

"You driving a Chevrolet weaving through traffic on Olympic chased by a dozen cop cars and my boss going, 'Wow, Christopher, is that your wife?' And me standing there like a bozo on acid. Then everyone we know started calling. Your mother was a nervous wreck. Even Barbara and Mum called."

"They saw it live in New Zealand? I thought it was in the middle of the night there."

"It was, but my Cousin John in London called Mum, woke her up and she saw the whole thing. Barbara too. It's been chaos here."

"Yeah, it's sort of been like that here, too."

"I just saw the news here in the airport…"

"You're in an airport? What airport?" I asked.

"Dallas Fort Worth. I'll be in LA in about three hours."

"That's so sweet. So you're not leaving me?" I bubbled.

"No, I'm not leaving you. But why didn't you tell me it was a publicity stunt? That's what they said on Fox News. I mean, it looked real on TV."

"I'll explain when I see you," I promised.

"What about the *Jane Blonde* deal? Is that actually happening?" Christopher asked.

"Sure is and everyone thinks we'll get a cool mil for it."

I heard him blow his nose, something he did when he was stressed.

"Get what?"

"A million. Dollars," I said.

I thought my call had been dropped, but I could still hear an airport announcement about his flight to LA boarding in the background.

"Honey? Did you hear what I said?"

"A million dollars?" he asked.

"That's what they say, but you know how things work in Hollywood."

He said something muffled to someone in the terminal and came back on the phone. "I have to board now. I'll call your cell when I get to LA."

"Okey dokey. Chris?"

"Yeah," He answered.

"I love you."

There was a long sigh, then he said, "I…" and then there was a click and a dial tone.

"Chris? Are you there?" I asked, knowing the call had been dropped. What was he going to say? Did he still love me?

I headed to LAX to find out.

On the way I to the airport I ran into traffic on Sepulveda. It didn't matter because Christopher's plane wouldn't land for another 3 hours. I probably could make it 10 miles by then.

I thought about Zaida and called her. The phone rang three times and I thought voice mail was going to pick up, but suddenly she answered breathlessly.

"Hello."

"Hey, Zaida, it's…"

She recognized my voice, cut me off for the first time in our 10-year relationship and shrieked, "Liz! I can't believe it. Oh, my God. I've been watching. I saw everything. I thought it was you when they started saying it was a deranged screenwriter."

"Thanks a lot."

"Then they started talking about *Jane Blonde* and I knew it was you. I couldn't figure out if it was the smartest thing I've seen you do or the dumbest. Then I saw the news conference about the deal and I knew you had it planned all along. That's why you said watch for breaking news on the TV, right?"

"Right. But…"

She interrupted again. I'd never seen her so fired up about anything. If she was this assertive about her writing career, she'd be in the WGA.

Zaida continued, "What I do not understand is how did you get LAPD and the Beverly Hills cops to go along?" Then there was a brief pause. "Oh, oh, oh. It wasn't really LAPD, was it? It was all staged. Like one big action stunt scene all choreographed, but shot in real time with studio choppers posing as Eye-in-the-Sky News, right? It was actually a set, not the real street, right?"

"Not exactly," I replied, wondering if I should tell her the truth. But what was the truth? I was getting confused myself.

"Was that really you driving? It sure looked like it. I called everyone in our writers group. They all saw it, except Tina who moved back to Madison to work in her uncle's cheese factory."

Tina was the most talented television writer in our group. Even though she had the most extraordinary writing samples for drama I've ever read, no one would hire her. In TV, writers had to be brilliant, and they also had to be good in the room. Most fictional shows were written with a group of writers slugging it out in a room.

You had to be brave enough to leap onto the table and scream, "I've got it. The seasonal finale is…" It could be anything. A main character is shot or burns down someone's house or is kidnapped. Whatever it was, you had to be able to shout and stamp your feet and throw fits until you got your way. Tina couldn't do that. So she was making cheddar for cheddarheads.

"Listen, Zaida, I'm almost to the airport and I've got to go, so…"

Zaida suddenly returned to her old timid self, "Oh, I thought maybe we could…but you're going home. Okay. Well…"

"I'm really sorry. I'd love to see you for dinner. I'll be back in a couple of weeks to meet with the studio folks and Gale Grazer, so we'll have sushi then. I promise."

Zaida giggled, "Okay then. Let me know and I'll get our old group together for a party at my house."

"I'll bring the champagne," I said.

When anyone in our writers group had something to celebrate, they brought champagne to the next meeting. I ended up bringing champagne a lot. I said goodbye to Zaida and turned into the short term parking garage at LAX.

I had two hours or so before Christopher's plane was scheduled to arrive. I wished I had brought my laptop to LA, so I could have worked on my new

Jane Blonde script. I knew I had to focus on something positive. I wandered through every shop in the concourse until I came to a wine bar with an impressive by-the-glass menu.

One glass of good zin with cheese and olives sounded perfect, so I perched on a black leather stool at a mahogany bar table. Unfortunately, a writer I'd met once when we were both faculty at a screenwriters conference cruise came in to wait for his wife's flight, delayed from Vancouver. Three glasses of zin and half a focaccia pizza later, I suddenly realized Christopher's plane should have landed 15 minutes earlier.

I promised to e-mail my friend and took off down the concourse. In a panic, I dashed past passengers to get to baggage claim, when I heard someone call my name.

I looked around and saw Christopher.

It was like one of those movie scenes where star-crossed lovers see each other for the first time in 20 years. Everything around them disappears, and it's only them gazing into each other's eyes, hearts beating as one. Except that my blood alcohol was near the California legal limit and I stumbled over a baby stroller pushed by a postpartum psycho-mom who whacked me with her diaper bag.

I lost my balance and fell toward Christopher. He caught me and pulled me to safety out of the flood of travelers. I looked up at him. In that instant, I remembered him sleeping when I left home wondering if I would ever see him again. Emotion rushed to my head.

Falling into his arms, I began weeping. It wasn't a defenseless woman boo-hoo, but more of a tears-of-joy boo-hoo brought on by the realization that my self-inflicted ordeal had ended well, and Christopher hadn't abandoned me. Yet.

Airports were a natural place for tears, with people parting and coming back together again, so I let her rip. Christopher had rarely seen me weep and

I think my public display of vulnerability embarrassed him. He held me close.

After ruining his favorite pin-striped work shirt with runny mascara, I calmed down enough to engage in a civil conversation.

"I thought you were going to get yourself killed," Christopher said. "You know I love you, but you're going to have to get control of yourself."

He still loved me. That was the best news I'd had all day, with the exception of getting out of jail free and becoming Hollywood's newest writer millionaire.

"When you used to say you were going to kick someone's ass, I thought it was a figure of speech, some redneck joke or something," Christopher continued. "It never occurred to me you would ever actually have a go at kicking Hollywood's collective ass."

Hell-A Rule #47: Speak softly and carry a big gun.

"It never occurred to me, either," I confessed. "The whole thing just sort of took on a life of its own. But…the most important thing is the happy ending, right?"

Christopher shook his head and replied, "Promise you will never, ever do anything like this again."

"That sounds familiar."

"Promise me." Christopher sounded serious.

"I promise," I said with my fingers crossed behind my back.

"You have your fingers crossed behind your back, don't you?"

He knew me too well.

There was a moment between us and then we both started laughing.

I was the luckiest woman in the world and I knew it. Christopher was the only man who could put up with my madness and still love me for the natural-born mess I was.

Chapter Sixteen

SAPPY ENDINGS

The World, Future.

The short hostage standoff at Nevison, the police convergence upon Ms. Portman's estate and our subsequent live-televised escape from the mansion, the worldwide coverage of the chase and champagne bar siege create an appetite for all things *Jane Blonde*—even before one frame of the movie is shot. The studio's marketing department goes into triple overtime for months making product placement deals, corralling fast-food partners, licensing *Jane Blonde* action figures and milking the film for every marketing dollar.

Florida, Future.

There's no place like a home on the beach. Which is what Christopher and I buy as soon as I get back to Florida.

I rewrite the script with notes from Katie, Gale, Steven, the studio head, Fireball, Zen Man, my new agent, my new manager, my new publicist, and my hair stylist. I even get notes from Chief Walker.

How he got the script, I'll never know. But, remarkably, he had some pretty good suggestions for some of the action scenes. Of course, he sent his own action script for me to read, which I stacked on the floor in my garage with all the other scripts I plan to read for other writers, when I have some incurable disease and am perpetually bedridden.

My million-dollar payday allows Christopher to quit his beloved nine-to-five job and devote his time to photography and making beer. For research we will travel to Cannes where the next *Jane Blonde* script will take place. Christopher's photos are shown at a local gallery and he forgives me for my insomnia-induced rampage in Hollywood.

I start sleeping straight through the starry Florida nights, my dreams filled with optimism and flying.

New Zealand, Future.

We go to New Zealand to visit Christopher's sister and mum. I discover I am a minor celebrity there and get to make a speech to the New Zealand Writers Guild about working in Hollywood. Of course, I don't tell them the whole truth and nothing but the truth. Nobody wants to hear about the grim, only the glitter.

We also get to hang out with Zen Man, Fireball, Gale, Steven, the studio head, Katie, and Hugh on the *Jane Blonde* set for a week of principal photography near Nelson in New Zealand's South Island. Oh, yeah, Hugh Farrell's agent is sleeping with Gale's casting director, so he gets the male lead without even auditioning.

Zen Man buys a place in the North Island where he plans to offer retreats for war-weary entertainment attorneys from LA and New York City. Fireball sets up three other movies after the *Jane Blonde* deal closes and buys a place next door to Zen Man to open a retreat for burned-out screenwriters. I promise to lecture there when I'm in-country.

Christopher proposes marriage again and we decide to elope. We don't tell anyone, not even our families. As we fly down to New Zealand's adventure playground of Queenstown, one of the engines goes out on the plane and we crash land in a field of sheep. Miraculously, no one is hurt seriously. This time we both agree to forget about getting married and do the wine tour of Central Otago instead. We're glad we didn't tell the folks.

We buy a house overlooking the Marlborough Sounds in the South Island where part of the movie is shot. We're thinking about even buying a vineyard. You can't beat Marlborough Sauvignon Blanc. Of course, the flight to Hell-A for business is long — 12 hours.

But 12 hours in first class isn't the worst way to spend time. And since New Zealand is the hot place to shoot film, producers and directors I work with jump at the chance for a "business trip" to Kiwiland, especially since our guest accommodations overlook the garden with rolling hills and bright blue water in the background. We call it the Nirvana Room. The all-you-can-drink wine is an attractive feature as well. Hollywood dealmaking goes better over several bottles of vino.

Hollywood, Future.

Speaking of vino, Nevison fires David, my evil former agent, after finding out about David bonking his wife and raiding the company coffers. David goes on a pinot noir bender and smashes up Nevison's office. David rebounds by opening his own management firm and embezzling his clients' money, which earns him three years in the state pen as someone's bitch.

I sue Jimmy Tremont for stealing my *Baja Triangle* script and 30 other victimized former clients join in. We win a million dollars each, although none of us ever expect to see the money since Jimmy is disbarred, declares bankruptcy, and moves to New Delhi to become a Bollywood producer. I'm sure to see *Bombay Triangle* on DVD soon.

Jason and Fifi become a couple and both flee the horrors of Hollywood to open a Chinese buffet restaurant in Santa Fe. It fails and they move in with Fifi's family in Mexico.

Tiffany becomes the V.P. of Production at Fox. Her newest movie, *Revenge of the Girly Girls,* is a smash at the box office.

Oh, and my friend Zaida wins a big writing award that allows her to write her first novel, which goes on to be a best-seller.

Life is beautiful.

Jane Blonde premieres in Tinseltown. The studio flies Christopher and me over to LA, picks us up in a shiny new limo, and puts us up at the posh Beverly Hills Hotel. It's all expenses paid, so we take a dozen of our closest friends for dinner at the newest scene restaurant in town.

> *Hell-A Rule #48: The most expensive food comes out first. If you're with an extravagant group and you're stupid, poor and order the chicken, with no appetizer, soup, salad, or $15 martinis, then your dinner arrives when everyone else is eating their desserts and sipping their Cognacs.*

Since the studio was paying, we all order the most expensive things on the menu and are served simultaneously by an armada wait staff. Celebrities greet us since they recognize me from my mug shot that was plastered on the front page of the *Los Angeles Times* after the kidnapping publicity stunt.

I am queen of the world!

We go to the *Jane Blonde* premiere and after-party with Zen Man, Fireball, and the studio head, who is Fireball's newest poker buddy. My new Stars&Lit agent is there fielding offers for my next project. My faith in literary representation has been restored, at least until he screws me.

Hell-A Rule #49: A great agent is impossible to find, but when you find one, only take them hostage as a last resort.

I wish I could say the premiere is an exciting time, but the truth is, after struggling in the film business for 10 years, I am in acute, brain-numbing shock the whole time. Being catapulted to the A-List is a bit like dying, I suspect. You aren't aware of the transition occurring until you're there, and then it doesn't really matter because you've transcended.

God bless Hollywood.

THE END

ABOUT THE AUTHOR

Sharon Y. Cobb

Form follows thought. If you can imagine any-
thing, you can do anything. Almost. For me,
that means living on an island and working as an
artist. It means getting in a formula car, revving
to 5000 rpms and popping the clutch. It means
going to Hollywood in search of movie studios
to pay me to write scripts. It means standing at
the edge of the cliff of the unknown and taking a
running leap. Life is a gift. Don't waste it doing
the dishes.

If the madcap adventures of Liz Bradbury inspire you to take one small step
out of your comfort zone to begin the journey that leads to fulfillment of your
creative dreams, please look for more Liz Bradbury/False Confessions books.

Sharon is a professional screenwriter and member of the Writers Guild of
America west. She has sold over a dozen projects to Hollywood and had some
films made. One of her favorites is Lighthouse Hill starring Jason Flemyng.
She also wrote a book called Touched by an Angel, A Christmas Miracle based
on the popular television program. She's won some screenwriting awards, but
not an Oscar, although she would happily accept one, if offered. She lives in
Florida with her tall husband Robert and short dog Carrie.

Sharon would love to hear from you on FaceBook at Hollywood House Publishing. Visit her author website at www.SharonYCobb.com. Get your daily
laugh at Sharon's funny video website, www.FunnyFixx.com. And if you're a
writer and would like to connect with agents and Hollywood producers, check
out Sharon's website, www.WritersPitchBook.com.

CPSIA information can be obtained at www.ICGtesting.com
Printed in the USA
LVOW010020011111

252767LV00003B/4/P